September 1944.

From the I.H.Q. Medical
Section of The Salvation
Army to Captain Mary
Campbell.

Jane Woodhouse.
Catherine Lobban
Catherine Dix.

IT BEGAN WITH ANDREWS

IT BEGAN
WITH ANDREWS

[The Saga of a Medical Mission]

by

Miriam M. Richards

with a foreword by
Brigadier The Right Hon. Sir John Smyth, Bt.,
V.C., M.C.

LONDON: Salvationist Publishing and Supplies, Ltd.

© The Salvation Army 1971

First published 1971

SBN 85412 202 8

Lieut.-Colonel Miriam Richards
is a Salvation Army officer who, from 1933 until her
retirement in 1971, has served in Great Britain in corps,
training, social, editorial and literary work. She is the
author of a wide range of books, including a number of
textbooks for Salvationist workers amongst children.

MADE AND PRINTED IN GREAT BRITAIN
IN GARAMOND TYPE BY
THE CAMPFIELD PRESS, ST. ALBANS, HERTS.

CONTENTS

PAGE

FOREWORD. By Brigadier the Rt. Hon. Sir John Smyth,
Bt., V.C., M.C. vii
INTRODUCTION. By Colonel Daniel Andersen, M.D. (Lon.),
F.R.C.S. (Eng.), D.T.M. & H. (Liv.) x
ACKNOWLEDGMENTS xv
ILLUSTRATIONS xviii

PART ONE

Pioneers! O Pioneers!

1. THE BRAVE ONE (Harry Andrews) 3
2. HE SET THE STANDARDS (Percy Turner) 9
3. NOT MERELY A DOCTOR (Charles Steibel) 16
4. SIGHT FOR THE BLIND (Vilhelm Wille) 22
5. CALLED TO LIVE FOR THE POOR (Sanya Matsuda) .. 27
6. SHE EASED THE WAY FOR OTHERS (Rin Iwasa) .. 30
7. HE GAVE ALL HE HAD (Arthur Swain) 33

PART TWO

Following the Trail

1. WILLIAM NOBLE (U.S.A.) 41
2. A. BRAMWELL COOK (New Zealand) 45
3. STANLEY BEER (England) 50
4. MARGARET ROUND (England) 52
5. CLESSON AND MARY RICHARDSON (U.S.A.) 55
6. DANIEL AND SÖLVI ANDERSEN (England and Norway) 57
7. WILLIAM McALLISTER (Scotland) 62
8. HARRY WILLIAMS (England) 67
9. SIDNEY GAUNTLETT (England) 72
10. SARA DANIEL (India) 75
11. K. C. JOSEPH (India) 77
12. CLIFFORD SEAMANS (U.S.A.) 78
13. TARO NAGASAKI (Japan) 81
14. LYLE ALLOWAY (U.S.A.) 83

PART THREE

Vital Co-operation

1. THE VALIANT NURSES 87
2. IN A NEAR-STONE-AGE WORLD 101
3. OVER THE HILLS AND FAR AWAY 111
4. HOW FAITH AND WORKS BUILT A HOSPITAL 116
5. TRAINING PROGRAMMES 122

PART FOUR

Tackling Needs in Many Lands

1. TUBERCULOSIS 135
2. LEPROSY 140
3. FRESH HOPE FOR THE HANDICAPPED 148
4. MINISTRY TO THE NEEDY IN THE SOUTH AMERICAN
   CONTINENT 161
5. MEDICAL WORK IN AFRICA 168
6. MEETING PRESENT NEEDS IN INDIA 174
7. WHAT OF TOMORROW? 178

BIBLIOGRAPHY 185

FOREWORD

by

Brigadier

The Rt. Hon. Sir John Smyth, Bt., V.C., M.C.

I AM indeed honoured to have been invited to write a foreword to this splendid book. I have always been a great admirer of the work of The Salvation Army and my wife and I had close relationships with Salvationists whilst I was Member of Parliament for Norwood in the Borough of Lambeth.

Their enthusiasm and the gladness of their Christianity was contagious and inspiring—and their complete dedication to their tasks of mercy was altogether admirable.

It so happened that in an action with the fierce tribesmen on the North-West Frontier of India, shortly after the First World War, I was thrown into contact with one of their most distinguished medical missionaries who had become an officer in the Indian Medical Service.

The action is referred to in the first chapter of this book.

Temporary Captain Henry John Andrews, M.B.E., had been an officer in The Salvation Army for over thirty years and was therefore not a young man at this time. He was a Senior Medical Officer at Khajuri Post at one end of the Shinki Pass, which was an important defended post on the lines of communication within the area of the 43rd Infantry Brigade of which I was Brigade Major. A very long and important animal transport convoy, over seven miles in length, was on its way up the line. A raiding party of about a hundred Mahsuds, the toughest of all the North-West Frontier tribesmen, had come down the night before and hidden themselves amongst the rocks at the side of the road. They waited until the head of the convoy had reached Khajuri Post and then opened fire, creating great havoc and causing a large number of casualties in men and animals.

But the officer commanding Khajuri Post had telephoned to Brigade Headquarters and the Brigade Commander sent me off at once with 300 Indian soldiers of the 9th Jats in Ford vans with two rather antiquated armoured cars. On our arrival a very hectic engagement took place in which the Mahsuds were eventually routed. Captain Andrews, quite regardless of his own danger, had only one thought—to collect the wounded, dress them quickly and send them off to safety in some of our Ford vans, which I had put at his disposal. He seemed to bear a charmed life as a number of his assistants were killed or wounded. Just as he was about to step into the last van, however, he was killed.

I brought his gallantry to the notice of my Brigadier and he was awarded a well-deserved posthumous Victoria Cross.

Captain Andrews had acted in accordance with the highest traditions of the Indian Medical Service and also of The Salvation Army.

This book records a number of stirring stories of the work of medical missionaries of The Salvation Army, in different parts of the world—including the Far East.

They are stories of very dedicated men and women working often in appallingly difficult conditions. Medicine and Christianity have often gone hand in hand, the one paving the way for the other.

The chapter on ' The Valiant Nurses ', some of them the wives of medical missionaries, and working closely with them, is particularly interesting and inspiring. Mrs. Colonel Percy Turner was the first registered nurse to function in such a capacity at the Catherine Booth Hospital, in South India, which her husband had founded.

Mrs. Turner had been trained as a nurse at Maidstone, England, and had proved her capacity in The Salvation Army's Women's Social Services at Ivy House, the first Salvation Army hospital, which had been opened in Hackney for maternity work and the training of midwives. She travelled to India in 1902 to become the wife of the ' Catherine Booth's ' first qualified medical officer. From the first she assisted her husband wholeheartedly in his hospital work. She did not allow the birth of two sons and a daughter to cool her ardour for her medical work in the slightest.

The Catherine Booth Hospital also did an invaluable service in training nurses both British and Indian.

There are many other remarkable stories of Salvation Army nurses who gave their lives to their job and became much beloved by all those with whom they worked—and particularly by their grateful patients.

The chapter on leprosy is both exciting and enlightening. Left untreated, this fell disease caused unparalleled suffering. The Salvation Army medical missionaries were able to make a considerable advance with regard to the care and treatment of leprosy patients—and most particularly of their children.

There are also valuable chapters on the ministry to the needy in the South American Continent, Salvation Army medical work in Africa; and supportive work in the West Indies, East Africa, India, Pakistan and Hong Kong, which is giving fresh hope to the handicapped.

The book ends with a chapter, 'What of Tomorrow?' If The Salvation Army's medical missionary service is as devoted and successful in the future as it has been in the past then it will be glorious indeed.

JACKIE SMYTH.

INTRODUCTION

By Colonel DANIEL ANDERSEN

M.D. (Lon.), F.R.C.S. (Eng.), D.T.M. & H. (Liv.)

THE story of the beginning of Methodism by John and Charles Wesley, at Oxford in 1729, is well known, but a lesser-known fact is that their elder brother Samuel, together with a banker Henry Hoare, and others, founded the first voluntary hospital in England in 1720.

The older hospitals, St. Thomas' and St. Bartholomew's, both religious foundations, had by then come under the control of Government and a fee was charged which made admission difficult for the neediest for whose help they had originally been intended.

The Westminster Public Infirmary was opened at the expense of the founders ' to find some remedy for the great misery of our neighbours '. Out of this beginning developed first St. George's Hospital and then the great voluntary hospital system, which established a fine tradition of medical care until it was incorporated into the National Health Service in 1948. Its tradition still persists in many ways.

The same outworking of a strong religious impulse in practical care for the whole man is shown in the story of the medical work of The Salvation Army recorded in this book. The medical story has two aspects: one seeking to meet urgent needs of the countries in which the work began; and the other in an outreach, a generation later, to distant lands still more needy.

The work in the ' western ' world has grown from homes for unmarried mothers in the 1880's to maternity and general hospitals by 1920, and today provides over 8,000 beds in eighty-four hospitals and nursing homes, including several large modern hospitals attached to teaching institutions in Canada and the U.S.A. But that is another story yet to be told.

This book ' begins with Andrews ', who founded the Catherine Booth Dispensary in South India, and his fellow-pioneers at the turn of the nineteenth century, continues with the story of the next generation ' who followed on ' and goes on to describe the third generation now active in seventeen developing countries, where they seek to play a part in solving medical problems which, perhaps with greater awareness, seem to be even greater than at the commencement of the twentieth century.

An aim that already shows some degree of fulfilment is that the future teams providing medical care in Salvation Army hospitals and clinics generally will be composed primarily of the people of these rapidly developing countries, assisted by their colleagues from other lands. In this field some of the missionary societies founded a century and more earlier have made greater progress, but we now have an active scholarship programme for training doctors, nurses and para-medical workers.

A unifying feature as evident today as at its beginning is the spontaneity of the response of individuals seeking to meet needs as they are seen, often in spite of many difficulties and sometimes of active discouragement, which is surely the authentic individual response to ' the love of God spread abroad in our hearts by the Holy Ghost '.

However, even Topsy who ' just grow'd ' had to be trained in a family, and the most encouraging fact of today is that we are learning to plan together.

G. K. Chesterton expressed this in his own fashion:

> I have therefore come to the conclusion that there is a complete contemporary fallacy about the liberty of individual ideas; that such flowers grow best in a garden and even grow biggest in a garden; and that in the wilderness they wither and die.

Ten years ago there were some medical missionary planners who felt that the day of overseas medical work was coming to an end. Their argument was, and still is in some quarters, that as the Governments in the developing countries improved their medical services, medical work by missionary societies would become redundant, and in any case the rising cost of modern medical care made it an uneconomical use of the limited money available.

In our own experience this view fails to be realistic about the overwhelming medical needs in developing countries today and the part that mission hospitals still need to play, in increasing co-operation both with the Government medical services and on an inter-mission basis.

In the District of Ahmednagar, for example, where my wife and I had the privilege of serving for twenty-one years, a survey over ten years ago indicated that the total medical services, including Government, private and mission hospitals, reached only about 30 per cent of the needs of the people. In spite of considerable development in the size and scope of all these medical services, a population increase of over 25 per cent in the last ten years has negatived such advances as would otherwise have been made. This carries an obvious lesson.

We do not, however, feel that the solution is bigger and more expensive mission hospitals, but rather

(a) A modernization within reasonable limits according to the local needs and with special reference to the needs of effective local training programmes, traditionally of nurses, but also of paramedical workers of various kinds.

(b) An extension outwards from a *base* district hospital to meet more directly, and as cheaply as consistent with effectiveness, the needs of the people at village level, with an emphasis on prevention, concentrating on the needs of children and mothers, including a major emphasis on family planning advice within the overall health programme.

This new outlook needs major adjustments in training programmes and planning at all levels.

There have been several developments in the last ten years providing new resources:

Drugs. With the active co-operation of the national Salvation Army headquarters, we have received generous free drug supplies through American, British, Dutch, German and Scandinavian inter-church or charitable organizations, subject to the payment of the cost of handling and transport in most cases.

Medical supplies. Five years ago the Medical Committee of the Conference of British Missionary Societies initiated a project, the Joint Mission Hospital Equipment Board, to provide good quality second-hand equipment of all sorts at a cost of 10–30 per cent of new articles, working in co-operation with the National Health Service.

Approved project support. This has been provided generously by The Salvation Army in many countries as well as from organizations such as OXFAM, Save the Children Fund, Emmaus Suisse, SIMAVI. Many individual donors and small groups have also helped generously. At the same time inter-church organizations in Norway, Holland, Germany and Switzerland, in co-operation with the 'private sector' of Government Aid to Developing Countries, have provided substantial financial aid for special projects approved by both the giving and receiving Governments. It is highly significant that whereas this aid is non-sectarian and can be given to any recognized organization, about 80 per cent in some countries has been allocated to the church-related medical work for reasons of economy and effectiveness.

Staff. There has been a needed and welcome increase in the number of doctors with good post-graduate experience offering for whole-time service as Salvation Army officers in the last few years, doubling our officer medical staff in this decade. There has also been a gradual increase in nursing and paramedical officer staff. Our urgent staffing needs have in several instances been met by ' short term ' doctors who have ' held the fort ' until permanent staff could take over. In addition, short term doctors, nurses and technicians have come for periods of one to three years to give needed support. Often these have belonged to denominations other than The Salvation Army. Finally, we have welcomed over a dozen final year medical students for their three months ' elective periods ' who have brought youthful zest and critical appreciation to our mutual benefit.

All these have provided a new climate for ' medical missionary work ' which is gradually changing its name and pattern to be ' Christian medical services ' in co-operation with the people and Governments of the countries concerned.

In a recently published report (1969) of the Commission on International Development, under the Chairmanship of Lester B. Pearson, emphasis is given to the special contribution that can and needs to be made by voluntary and private organizations. Among these Christian churches and missions play a substantial part. It points out:

(1) That the number of persons engaged in this kind of work in low income countries has increased fivefold in the last six years.

(2) That such organizations possess the following special advantages over both large official aid agencies and private corporation investors:

(a) They are able to undertake vitally useful but modestly sized projects.

(b) They can provide support for ' experimental ' ventures, which can later be extended.

(c) It is generally easier to preserve mutual self-respect in private aid activities.

There is surely a continuing challenge to the world-wide Christian Church to continue to share in this valuable partnership, and be worthy followers of our medical forebears. Many of these have been pioneers such as Dr. Ida Scudder in Vellore, Dame Edith Brown of Ludhiana and Dr. William Wanless of Miraj in education; Drs. Frimodt Möller (Senior and Junior) in tuberculosis,

Drs. Cochrane and Paul Brand in leprosy, and Dr. Gladys Rutherford in village health, to take examples from India only.

However, we would be far from realistic if we minimized the increased cost of such effective medical help with a Christian background. While new capital resources are available, they are still small in relation to the overall need, and an increasingly felt need is for more maintenance support which is the primary responsibility of the Christian body which endeavours to continue the great medical missionary tradition of the past in the modern context.

Personal giving is still too small and too spasmodic and this book is a new call to us all to put more realism into our acceptance of our Lord's command to 'love our neighbour as ourselves'. We still need the divine compassion working in and through us and, while doing our *duty* in sharing our material benefits with fellow human beings, we can, as personal Christians and in the spirit of our pioneers, also humbly 'hold forth the bread of life'.

The saga related here—and I think it deserves the name—is necessarily incomplete. For example, in *All the World* for April 1899, we read of an International Headquarters Medical Department with two doctors, Major Williams and Ensign Hart, who looked after the health of officers and employees in the United Kingdom and advised about overseas work. This start was not maintained and we can find out little about it today: but they and many others both named and unnamed have contributed by service, financial support and prayer to whatever has been accomplished.

We look ahead in faith with the certainty that God will continue to speak to the hearts of men and women and that many will respond.

ACKNOWLEDGMENTS

THE originator of the idea for this book is Colonel (Dr.) Daniel Andersen, Medical Missionary Secretary at the International Headquarters of The Salvation Army, London, whose first intention it was to make available for all who might be interested in offering personal or financial help to centres of the work in various parts of the world *a directory of The Salvation Army's medical missionary services*. Brigadier (Dr.) Sidney Gauntlett has been responsible for the collection, sub-editing and collation of this material.

Feeling it necessary in addition to the directory to provide information about the pioneers of The Salvation Army's medical missionary work, Colonel (Dr.) Andersen made an approach, early in 1970, to the Literary Secretary at International Head-quarters, then Colonel Thos. Lewis, and the seed which has borne fruit in the present volume was sown. Once recorded, the stories of the pioneers seemed to demand that something be said about their immediate successors, and so the plan for the book developed. The suggestion that such a volume should be prepared was accepted by the Book Programme Council, headed by The Salvation Army's International Leader, General Erik Wickberg, and the work of research, compilation and editing went forward.

It is a particular honour to have had the foreword to the completed book written by Brigadier The Right Hon. Sir John Smyth, Bt., V.C., M.C., who here reveals that the posthumous award of the Victoria Cross to Harry Andrews, the 'Andrews' of the book's title, came as the result of his drawing attention to the gallantry of this compassionate man, whose life-saving action under fire he witnessed.

Thanks are due to numerous individuals who have made available personal papers, photographs and other records concerning the pioneers. These include:

Mrs. Jean Biggs, grand-daughter of Harry Andrews, and her mother, Mrs. Reginald Andrews; Colonel Catherine Baird (R.), who had earlier made a collection of information about Colonel Percy Turner from members of his family, including Dr. Cyril Turner and Mr. Aidan Turner, and from his former colleagues, as well as securing a great deal of material about the beginnings of Salvationist medical missionary work in India, Africa and Indonesia; Mr. Basil Richards, grandson of Percy

Turner; Lieut.-Commissioner (Dr.) Harry Williams, now Territorial Commander, New Zealand, who, for his unpublished MS about Charles Steibel, which he entitled ' The Shy Soldier ', had made considerable on-the-spot research in India and had also had access to Mrs. Agatha Steibel's privately published journal; Mrs. Lieut.-Colonel Ellen Wille (R.), Denmark, widow of Lieut.-Colonel Vilhelm Wille; Lieut.-Colonel Thorsten Kjäll, of Sweden, and Colonel Wm. Larson, at the time Chief Secretary for Denmark, who helped to secure the books written in Danish about Vilhelm Wille by his son, Johannes Wille, extracts from which were translated into English by Senior-Major Elisabeth Balshaitis; Colonel Arthur Ludbrook (R.), who contributed reminiscences of Dr. Arthur Swain and loaned his personal copies of *The Crusader*; Colonel (Dr.) Wm. and Mrs. Noble (R.) who, during a visit to International Headquarters in 1970, were able to contribute valuable supplementary information about the pioneers in India, and Lieut.-Colonel Cyril Barnes, Assistant Literary Secretary, International Headquarters, whose painstaking collection of previously published information on Salvationist medical missionary work, has been a rich source of help.

Earlier publications to which reference is made are listed in the Bibliography.

Colonel (Dr.) Daniel Andersen and members of his office staff, including Brigadier Lilian Leib (R.), Miss Margaret Hitcham and Miss Sybil Chivers, have been meticulous in providing lists of medical personnel, past and present, though it is recognized that only sparse records exist of some earlier medical missionary helpers, who have included such valued workers as Dr. Johansson, a Swede with a large family (mentioned in The Salvation Army Year Book for 1919) who gave a number of years' service in India, including a period at Anand, and Dr. Muir (referred to in the Year Book for 1935) who served at Adoor (later known as Koratty). Some of those who had given earlier service overseas were, happily, able to furnish particulars of their own contributions, whilst in respect of others it has been necessary to rely on The Salvation Army Year Book, other more personal records having been lost in war-time destruction. Unwittingly, omissions may also have been due to such loss.

Supplementary information about the service of certain doctors, and of the valiant nurses who have also tended the needy sick, has been supplied by:

Colonel Arthur Linnett, formerly Editor-in-Chief, Australia

Southern Territory, and now Literary Secretary, International Headquarters, and staff of the Overseas Departments at International Headquarters, including Colonel Frank Hutchins, Brigadier Ron Cox, Majors Chas. Durman and Leslie Pull, Brigadier Marie Cunningham, Brigadier Nellie Kellow and Brigadier Muriel Linkins, as well as Brigadier Catherine Rendell (R.), Brigadier Ethel Neeve (R.), Major Agnes Cage, International Headquarters, and Captain Jessie Jenks, Papua/New Guinea.

Lieut.-Commissioner (Dr.) Harry Williams, Colonel (Dr.) Wm. McAllister, now Chief Secretary, Men's Social Services in Great Britain and Ireland, and Brigadier (Dr.) Sidney Gauntlett, Medical Officer for the International Training College, London, in personal contact and by correspondence were able to provide unique information about fields of which they have specialist knowledge by reason of their own experience in medical missionary service, e.g. leprosy treatment, reconstructive surgery and rehabilitation programmes, nurse training programmes and so on.

In the articles dealing with specific aspects of the medical (and supportive) work, main contributors are usually mentioned by name. Supplementary information has also been supplied by:

Lieut.-Commissioner W. Stanley Cottrill, as Secretary to the Chief of the Staff (now of Korea); Lieut.-Commissioner F. Frank Saunders (Territorial Commander), Major Bernard Wicks and Mrs. Major Janet Parkes, Caribbean and Central America Territory; Major Doreen Hobbs, International Headquarters; Colonel Joseph Dex (Territorial Commander) and Major Carl Eliasen (General Secretary), Brazil; Lieut.-Commissioner Per-Erik Wahlström (Territorial Commander), South America East; and by Lieut.-Commissioner Harry Tyndal (Territorial Commander), Denmark.

A large amount of typing and re-typing of material has been undertaken by Mrs. Major Gordon Sharp and Miss Betty Lowe, to whom—with all the foregoing—our heartfelt thanks are recorded.

MIRIAM M. RICHARDS.

ILLUSTRATIONS

facing page

Harry Andrews 78

Catherine Booth Hospital, Nagercoil, India 78

Weaving, for leprosy patients, Nagercoil 78

Percy Turner 78

Public health teaching in a village school, India 79

Having fun at ' Joytown ', Kenya 79

Arriving at Howard Hospital, Rhodesia 79

Dental surgery in São Paulo, Brazil 94

In a rural area, Korea 94

H.I.H. Princess Chichibu at the opening of the Booth
    Memorial Hospital, Tokyo 94

Dispensary at Moungali, Brazzaville 95

Tuberculosis ward at Ahmednagar, India 95

PART ONE

Pioneers! O Pioneers!

THE BRAVE ONE

Chapter
One

HARRY ANDREWS

IT was love for people and concern for their physical and spiritual welfare that led Bramwell Booth, son of The Salvation Army's Founder, living in the early 1870's in the East End of London, to visit families in certain workmen's cottages in the vicinity of Victoria Park. When he promised to care for a dying mother's baby boy he was not to know that he was cherishing a seed from which would spring a vital harvest in the field of medical missionary work. Nor could he have guessed that the tiny infant, then so dependent, would as a nineteenth-century missionary be given the Indian name, Sekundar (The Brave One). The name proved one that its bearer was supremely fitted to hold, for at the close of his life, shortly after the First World War, he was to merit the Victoria Cross.

Henry John Andrews, early a motherless child, was in 1873 lovingly received to be cared for, first at home and then in a nursery at Clapton with others, by Bramwell's sister, Emma. In 1888, when young Harry was fifteen, Emma Booth became the wife of Frederick de Lautour Tucker, pioneer of Salvation Army work in India, and the boy begged to accompany his beloved ' mother ' overseas. Soon afterwards, the gift of some dental instruments, sent to him in India from Bramwell Booth, set Harry Andrews on a course of practical helpfulness to the needy. In Bombay, dirt, poverty and pain were all around him. At least he could try to relieve the pain! It was not long before he became adept at wielding the dental forceps and the few other instruments at hand.

At the age of seventeen Harry became an officer in The Salvation Army. He was appointed to assist Major William Stevens, a one-time Worthing jeweller, at the headquarters in Nagercoil. Mrs. Stevens, becoming aware of the youth's practical sympathies and his keen desire to relieve suffering, observed, ' The boy wants to heal bodies and I'm going to make it easier for him. He shall have that little bathroom at the end of the verandah for a dispensary.'[1] (The bathroom door is today preserved in the structure of the Catherine Booth Hospital, Nagercoil, a telling link with the humble beginnings in Southern India of Salvationist medical service.)

3

The amateur dispensary in the bathroom was set up in 1893 and patients walked many miles to seek help at the hands of the young man with eyes to see and a heart to care deeply for their needs, to which was added ' a remarkable practical ability to meet those needs with the limited means at his disposal '.[2]

It was a severe outbreak of cholera in Travancore (today part of Kerala State) that first constituted Harry Andrews' call to an even wider field of medical work. Gathering a few simple remedies, he went from village to village, ministering to the sick and dying. To see suffering was to him a call to try to remedy it. From a neighbouring hospital he sought medicine and advice, and constant practice in all kinds of emergencies soon furnished him with valuable experience.

When news of Harry's skill was reported to The Salvation Army's London Headquarters, Bramwell Booth thought it worthwhile to bring the young officer to England to take a dresser's course in a London hospital. Returning to India in 1896, Andrews learned from Major Stevens with boyish delight the news that a friend had given £50 with which to purchase a piece of land where ' a proper dispensary ' could be erected. Visiting the chosen site, both men knelt in the open country to seek divine blessing on the project.

The dispensary, which rose on the spot, was a whitewashed mud-walled building with a grass-thatched roof that gave shade some feet outside the walls. It was named the Catherine Booth Dispensary in honour of the Army Mother, Co-Founder with William Booth of The Salvation Army. As the work grew, a larger building became necessary. Harry found a site, designed the new building and helped to dig its foundations.

Shortly before sailing for England, Harry Andrews had read a paragraph in *The War Cry* telling of a Captain Percy Turner, a young English doctor recently appointed to corps work at Lewisham, South London, and determined to seek him out. Percy Turner, a keen Salvationist who had been converted in 1887, shortly before becoming a medical student, had caused some astonishment among his colleagues at St. Bartholomew's Hospital in the City of London by appearing in their midst in Salvation Army uniform, but had soon become accepted among them with respect, for he proved himself no mean scholar. First among the students at ' Barts ' for the senior medical scholarship, he later carried off honours and two other scholarships at Durham University, beside securing a D.P.H. (Oxon.).

Becoming a Salvation Army officer, Turner had given up his

medical career (as he thought for ever) to devote himself to a life of evangelistic ministry, when in 1896 he found himself confronted one day by the earnest young man from India, with heart-rending descriptions of the need there for a qualified medical practitioner. Andrews told how he himself had sometimes sat up all night studying the treatment of diseases he would have to deal with next morning.

Having presented the challenge of medical work in India, Harry Andrews then used his powers in prevailing on Bramwell Booth to persuade William Booth to appoint Captain Percy Turner as the first qualified medical officer to the Catherine Booth centre at Nagercoil. Thereafter, while Harry Andrews returned to India, Percy Turner set to work to qualify himself yet more fully for the needs he now understood to exist in India. A period as a resident medical officer in the Ophthalmic Hospital at Maidstone, Kent, helped to give him practical experience in a field in which he was to render particularly valuable service in days to come. Harry Andrews, meantime, kept Captain Turner posted on the particular cases he was handling.

For Harry, marriage in 1899 to Ensign Gena Smith, who had shared his childhood home in the nursery established at Clapton by his beloved ' mother ', had given him a helpful partner in his work for the suffering. Bearing the Indian name of Devalee, signifying 'Light', his bride had already rendered sterling service as an officer for eight years, and for her part felt there could be no more suitable life partner than the fellow-missionary she had known and admired for so long.

In all the conversations and correspondence between Harry Andrews and Turner neither of them mentioned the question of salaries, though it is on record that ' when he was doing his most exacting and finest work, Harry Andrews took only eight rupees, and Turner with his wife, a qualified nurse, lived on thirty rupees a month, though when in 1900 he had arrived in Nagercoil he was offered a Government Hospital in Trivandrum with a salary of six hundred rupees a month '.

Dr. Turner took charge of the institution that had grown out of Harry Andrews' bathroom dispensary and with quiet skill and application, during the twenty-one years he was to spend in India as the Army's Chief Medical Officer, built up a worthy establishment, known as the Catherine Booth Hospital, Nagercoil, which was to contain a tiled building, complete with operating theatre and clinic laboratory. This became a vital centre from which eight branches were directed. For as long as he was required, Andrews helped the doctor whose many advantages, had he been less self-forgetful, he might have envied!

Though Andrews was then content to be transferred to Anand, in Gujerat, West India, and take up the ordinary duties of a Salvation Army missionary officer, believing his ' medical ' service to be at an end, it was not long before, with the coming of famine and attendant plague, his compassion again forced him to do all he could for the sick of the area. With clamant calls around him, Harry could not refuse to treat those who sought his help.

The need for some accommodation was soon clear and once again a hospital site was chosen, this time centrally situated in Anand. A Miss Elizabeth Julia Emery, born in Canada, of Gloucestershire parents, donated money in memory of her sister to found a hospital here. Andrews himself was architect and surveyor, and even head foreman of a gang of women who were engaged to help him build the new hospital, established in 1903 and to be known as the Emery Hospital.

When the plague struck again, ' the work of building was carried on with difficulty, for Harry's time was divided between supervising the erection of the hospital and tending the sick '.[1] But ' in spite of many interruptions the building went forward even to the sinking of a fine well. The operating theatre, when finished, was a model of up-to-date equipment, and the wide shady verandah made an inviting waiting room.

' Once more Andrews withdrew in favour of a qualified doctor, glad that it was becoming less difficult to find one. And now, too, the Army's Founder recognized the value of establishing a number of medical centres.

' Bramwell Booth, who had watched Harry's work in India, arranged for him to go to America to take his degree in medicine and surgery. In what spare time he had between his studies at the Illinois University he took any sort of job that would earn for him the money to pay his fees.'[1]

Qualified as a doctor at last, Harry Andrews returned in 1912 to India, this time to Moradabad in the North. Miss Emery had again made a generous donation—of £3,000 in this instance—to found a hospital in India as a memorial to her father. Established at Moradabad in 1913, it was to be known as the *Thomas* Emery Hospital. Under the energetic and able supervision of ' Dr. Sekundar ', blocks of buildings soon covered a great part of the twenty-acre ground, with room also provided for future extensions which he felt certain would be needed. The buildings attracted the admiration of all visitors, including military and medical experts.

During the 1914–18 war, military hospitals were taxed to their utmost capacity. Thus it came about that ' Government appealed for help in caring for the wounded and sick Indian soldiers who were returning from France and Mesopotamia ', and ' The Salvation Army placed the Thomas Emery Hospital of Moradabad, with its doctors and staff, at the disposal of the military authorities'. The doctor at that time was Harry Andrews, of whom Major-General Sir Patrick Hehir was to write in *The British Medical Journal*:

' He was a man with broad human sympathies . . . loved by the poor, and their care, comfort and treatment were meticulously attended to in his hospital. He was a good operator, and crowds of people flocked from various parts of the Moradabad district to be treated by him. He designed and supervised the construction of the Salvation Army hospital at Moradabad. It is a model of what a district hospital should be in India. It is one of the few hospitals in Oudh that has its own tube well. It was well organized and administered. The hospital was made over to the Government as a War Hospital in a whole-hearted manner by The Salvation Army, and did most laudable work for our sick and wounded Indian soldiers. . . .'[2]

At the end of the war, when troubles arose with warlike tribes on the North-West Frontier of India, the military authorities requisitioned the help of Dr. Andrews (now a Lieut.-Colonel in The Salvation Army) in the area where raids were taking place, giving him military rank as a temporary Captain. His personal letters at the time showed that his sympathies were drawn out towards the turbulent frontier tribesmen—people who seemed to have no alternative to starvation but robbing their neighbours in the adjoining fertile districts. The barren character of the country they inhabited, it seemed to him, called for bread rather than bullets. ' There are many sad things, I know, in England,' he wrote, ' but war is terrible and it will be a grand day when war shall be no more.'

' One night (October 22, 1919) when the moon shone white upon the sandy slopes, as senior officer he was in charge of the Khajuri post when word reached him that a convoy was being attacked. This he knew would mean many wounded. Some at least must be saved.'[1]

The London Gazette of September 10, 1920, records: ' He at once took out an aid post to the scene of action and, approaching under heavy fire, established an aid post under conditions which afforded some protection to the wounded but not to himself. Subsequently he was compelled to move his aid post to another position, and continued most devotedly to attend to the wounded. Finally, when a Ford van was available to remove the wounded, he showed the utmost disregard of danger in collecting the wounded under fire and placing them in the van.'

In 1965, which was The Salvation Army's Centenary Year, the presentation and unveiling of a painting (portraying the scene in which ' Captain Henry J. Andrews, I.M.S., who fell at Khajuri, Waziristan, on the North-West Frontier of India in 1919 ' won the Victoria Cross) took place in the V.C's room of the Headquarters Mess of the R.A.M.C., Millbank, London, where thirty-nine paintings represented as many other recipients of the Victoria Cross. Sir John Smyth was present at the ceremony, and gave a vivid picture of Andrews' action at the time. Here is how he has described the circumstances in his book, *The Story of the Victoria Cross:**

Temporary Captain Henry John Andrews, M.B.E., of the Indian Medical Service, was awarded a posthumous V.C. for his gallantry and self-sacrifice in Waziristan on the North-West Frontier of India, on October 22, 1919, in one of the grimmest little episodes in our long frontier history. He had been an officer in The Salvation Army in India for over thirty years so he was very much above the average age of V.C. winners—in fact, quite an elderly man. He was at this time the Senior Medical Officer in Khajuri post at one end of the Shinki Pass, which was an important defended post on the lines of communication within the area of the 43rd Infantry Brigade, of which I was Brigade Major. A very long and important animal transport convoy, over seven miles in length, was on its way up the line, protected by a number of road picquets, posted each day on either side of the road.

A raiding party of about a hundred Mahsuds, the toughest of all the North-West Frontier tribesmen, had come down the night before and hidden themselves in the rocks on one side of the road. They waited until the head of the convoy had reached Khajuri post and then opened fire, creating absolute havoc; the road became littered with dead and wounded men and animals. Then, keeping the road covered, they had only to wait a few hours for darkness to set in before they swept in, killing and looting. But the officer commanding Khajuri post got through on the telephone to Brigade Headquarters and the Brigade Commander sent me off at once with 300 men of the 9th Jats, under Captain McCalmont, in Ford vans and supported by two antiquated armoured cars.

We arrived on the scene within two hours and a very hectic scrap started in which the Mahsuds eventually had to call it a day. Captain Andrews, quite regardless of his own danger, had only one thought, to collect the wounded, dress their wounds and send them up the line in

* Published by Fredk. Muller Ltd., London, 1963.

some vans to the field hospital. A number of his assistants—and also some of the wounded—were killed, but Captain Andrews seemed to bear a charmed life, but just as he stepped into the last van on completion of his task he was killed.

Such was the selfless, God-fearing, compassionate man to whom The Salvation Army owes the foundation of its medical missionary work. 'The Brave One' has led the way for many others. Words which appear in an article, written jointly by himself and his wife for a private Salvation Army magazine, *The Officer*, in January 1916, are indicative of his outlook:

> On every hand there are boundless opportunities, but the great lack is the right men and women for this work. . . . There is always some devoted man or woman holding on in some lonely medical mission station . . . hoping against hope that this year or next relief will come. When it does come it is often too late, and the newcomer only fills a vacancy instead of an advance post. 'Pray ye therefore the Lord of the harvest, that He will send forth labourers into His harvest.'

Chapter
Two

HE SET
THE STANDARDS
PERCY TURNER

PERCY EDWARD HEDGMAN TURNER, born on March 10, 1870, was the eldest of seven children. His father, who was an apothecary, had, at the age of sixteen years, been apprenticed at the Apothecaries' Hall, London. Percy, at ten years of age, had already made up his mind to be a doctor. Earlier the boy had attended a large day-school at Islington. He discovered, when he was attempting to play cricket, that unfortunately he could not see the ball. The disability made for some loneliness in his school life and may have had some bearing on his later interest in ophthalmology. However, he compensated for his deprivation by immersing himself in his school work, and managed to gain entry to the first class, which was preparing for the Cambridge local examination, when he was only twelve.

The family later moved to Kensington and Percy was sent to an Anglo-Catholic boarding school at Hurstpierpoint, Sussex, where he remained until he was seventeen, securing the school leaving certificate at the end of the summer term, and intending to enter hospital for medical training in the following October. He had meantime been confirmed in the Anglican Church.

When, in 1887, the family visited Folkestone for a month's holiday, Percy went with them, and his mother, a woman of personality, soon discovered a local chemist who proved willing to accept her son as an apprentice. Instead of proceeding to the hospital, Percy found himself working with a particularly enter-prising man who ran a first-rate business and did his own manu-facturing in preference to buying wholesale. The experience was to stand Turner in good stead later.

With the departure of his family after their holiday, young Turner found himself somewhat alone, although an intellectual friendship with a young schoolmaster and an association with a bookseller, who allowed him to browse among his shelves, helped to ease the situation. Opposite the bookseller's premises was another business, owned by a man whose five daughters all helped in the shop. Sometimes the girls crossed the road and invaded the bookshop. Three of them proved to be Salvationists and some hot arguments arose between them and the young Anglo-Catholic. Finally, one of the girls said: ' Look here; you come to the Army and see for yourself!' Challenged in this way, young Turner retorted : 'All right; you take me!', but insisted on sitting well back in the hall.

To the gently-reared young man everything in the Salvation Army hall seemed at first a maze of sound and colour. The singing was loud and uninhibited. The men Salvationists all wore red jerseys. But young Turner had to agree that the people he saw seemed to be enjoying their religion. Their radiant happiness appealed to him. There was a ring of certainty about their testi-monies. Soon he was a seeker for the same personal experience of Christ.

One evening, singing with his new-found friends around the piano in their home a Moody and Sankey hymn with the assertion, ' I know He is mine ', he entered a new world and realized he had found a divine Saviour and Helper. 'As I went out afterwards and looked at the stars,' he confessed, ' I thought they had never been so bright before.' That was August 14, 1887.

About six months later he began his medical training. His parents were not at all pleased when he told them he had attended The Salvation Army. His desire, when he returned to London, was to seek out a local corps and begin regular attendance there, but he came to an arrangement with his mother that he would accompany her to Church in the morning and make his way to ' the Army ' at night. He wanted as soon as possible to align himself with these people, who would prove, he felt sure, much like the family he had met at Folkestone, who were ' religious all day long and were, with it all, jolly and happy '.[3]

At St. Bartholomew's Hospital, London, where he had begun his training, the Student Christian Association was particularly strong and the young medical student joined the group each week ' in the inquest room ', for their meeting. At Chelsea Corps, which he was now attending, he learned that Mrs. Catherine Booth was leading a series of meetings in the lower Exeter Hall, then situated in the Strand, each Thursday afternoon. By dint of getting help from some of his fellow-students, he managed to reach the hall by 2.45 on a Thursday afternoon, making this his recreation, his constant attendance testifying to the earnestness of his seeking spirit. What particularly attracted the young man was the holiness teaching he heard. After some six months, he made the life-changing decision which brought full commitment to Christ and service with The Salvation Army.

On the following Sunday young Turner announced to his father that he was going to join The Salvation Army, and at Chelsea that day received a copy of the Salvationist 'Articles of War ' which he took home, read through and found no difficulty in signing. Three weeks later saw his enrolment as a Salvation Army soldier. A young officer loaned him a red jacket until he was able to buy a uniform of his own. Turner was all for becoming an officer forthwith, but his father counselled finishing his medical training and waiting until he came of age. Salvation Army leaders, whom the father consulted, agreed and Turner went on with his studies.

When another student became a Christian and joined Percy Turner in becoming a Salvation Army soldier too, both young men decided they ought to wear uniform at the hospital. Having taken the decision, no chaffing would daunt them, and Turner's appearances in uniform at the hospital were remembered and talked of well into the next century by those who had noted his quiet but bold witness.

Years passed during which Turner, as well as proving himself a sound and proficient medical scholar, carried positions of some responsibility in the local corps at Chelsea. By the time he had gained his qualifications—the London M.R.C.S., L.R.C.P.—he felt constrained to re-apply for full-time service in The Salvation Army. At that time (1893) there seemed no prospect of his being able to use his medical knowledge as an officer but Turner felt assured that God was not inconsistent. He was qualified to be a doctor: he was called to be a Salvation Army officer. He had faith in a God who could not deny Himself. His application went forward and he became a cadet on February 2, 1894.

Following a brief period of Salvation Army officer-training at Clapton, and six months' 'field training' at Highgate, Turner received a letter appointing him to the staff of the training college, where he gave lectures and conducted medical examinations of men-cadets.

Later that year Captain Turner was sent with a Lieutenant to Dartford, where there had been a breakdown, and further 'field appointments' followed, at Forest Hill and Lewisham. It was while at the latter corps that in 1896 the historic meeting took place between him and Harry Andrews, at that time officially the Army's Assistant Inspector of Schools in India, who was obsessed with concern for the many sick and ailing people he met daily and had been trying to help. Said Turner, in after years: ' He was insistent with the "Come over and help us" plea. We sat by the fire and talked for long hours. He made me feel willing to go.'

The encounter with Andrews led Captain Turner to an interview with Bramwell Booth who, as Chief of the Staff, was his father's leading executive officer. Bramwell Booth outlined the opportunity The Salvation Army—in response to Harry Andrews' pleas—was willing to give the young doctor in India. But Turner demurred at any precipitate departure at this stage. ' By becoming an officer I had had no practice except a clinical assistant's post at an eye hospital while in the training college,' he afterwards wrote. ' I said that I must have practice.'

Turner felt that if The Salvation Army were to open up medical work officially they would need people of higher qualification than he yet possessed to give the work status. He proposed he be given two years' working furlough, to obtain medical practice and to gain the higher qualifications he felt would be in The Salvation Army's interests. He could graduate in that time with a university qualification. He saw William Booth himself, who told him: ' I have no leading on the subject, but if you think that is the best way, go and do it! ' Turner went and did it; and was interested to discover how much more fascinating his studies were, now that he had a vocation.

Passing his final examinations with the University of Durham, M.B., B.S., he was awarded the Luke Armstrong Scholarship in Surgery in 1899. He also took the D.P.H. (Oxford) in 1899. But Captain Turner still felt he must know more about the treatment of eye disorders and diseases, so prevalent were these in India. His request for a further extension of furlough was granted and he applied, and was accepted, for the post of Resident Surgeon at the eye hospital in Kent where he was destined to meet his future life-partner.

He observed of Sister Minnie Mayger, the nurse in charge of the children's ward, that she was ' an amazing person. She excited my wonder as to how she could keep a nursery of children in order and carry on other duties '. Turner made up his mind to ' find out her spiritual condition '. He invited her to a musical meeting at the Maidstone Corps. She, on her part, found the new doctor's religion ' attracted her from the first. It was so robust, joyful and confident '. Though she very much wished to accept the invitation, for some time she held aloof, and it was only later and with some purposeful avoidance of appearing to want Salvationism for the sake of the doctor, that she became a pledged Salvationist herself. ' To her relief in one sense, and her genuine regret in another, Dr. Turner took his departure for India.'[4]

That the new doctor soon found acceptance with the Indian people there could be no doubt. ' When the doctor arrived in Nagercoil,' one of them afterwards wrote, ' he was quite young and charming in his appearance. He looked every bit a polished English gentleman with a happy face and pleasing manner. . . . In talking to the people he was gentle in his ways and friendly in his contact—the people took to him straight away.' He was given the name of Dayanasen, ' Man of Loving Kindness '. ' He was very true to his name,' was the comment of another Indian comrade.

Two years later, when Minnie Mayger had herself become a Salvation Army officer, she received a letter from India asking her if she would become Percy Turner's ' continual comrade in the war ' (the Salvationist's term for his soldierly marriage-partner).

Meanwhile Ensign Turner had taken hold with both hands of the opportunity presented at the Catherine Booth Dispensary, Nagercoil. Commissioner T. Henry Howard—a Salvation Army leader with whom Turner had travelled to India in 1900—looked over the dispensary with its two tiny wards and offered the sum of ten pounds to build a much-needed new wing.

The original plan had been that Turner was to work with Harry Andrews—Sekundar, ' The Brave One '—for a year and then move to a chosen site and ' make an official start '; but local needs decided the issue and finally, with the erection of new wards for men and women, it became evident that Sekundar could not carry on without Turner's help. A doctor had become indispensable. An operating theatre and laboratory were put up, and separate kitchens built for Hindu and Mohammedan patients and their friends, who came to the hospital with them and stayed to cook their meals. Eventually it was Sekundar and his wife who moved on and Percy Turner, and his bride from England, who remained. 'I was sorry to lose such a good helper,' Turner admitted.

The doctor and his bride were married in October, 1902, in a remarkable out-door wedding ceremony watched by thousands. Soon they were fully occupied together in the hospital, the husband instructing Indian compounders in the skill of dispensing and Mrs. Turner beginning the training of Indian nurses. A near-miraculous recovery of his wife from serious illness gave the doctor—and the small but growing Indian staff—cause for deep rejoicing at answered prayer, and the work went steadily on.

Visiting the Maharajah of Travancore, Turner sought financial help for his project of four-year medical courses, with laboratory work and dissections within the hospital. With the help of another doctor, the courses were finally launched and the students given regular examinations according to the English syllabus. Three men eventually qualified for the Diploma, to be recognized by the letters L.M.S.M.G. (Licentiate in Medicine, Surgery, Midwifery and Gynaecology).

Among those who trained under Turner, three of the Salvation Army officers recognized as Registered Medical Practitioners in the Kerala State, Brigadier T. C. Chacko, Senior-Major S. Gnanaiah and Senior-Major J. Manuel, gave valuable service over many years.

In the last year or two of the course, Turner set about finding sites for branch hospitals. Two were built and another started before the Turners left for their first homeland furlough, in 1908. Two of the qualified men were put in charge of the couple of completed branch hospitals and the third man was left at the Catherine Booth Hospital. Percy Turner himself, during his furlough, took the M.D. (Durham) qualification.

In 1917 Turner wrote of the *four* branch hospitals then established in the area surrounding the Catherine Booth Hospital: ' The latter are truly branches, for in origin have they sprung from the original stock, in method of growth and appearance they are like it; and in fruit, most important of all, they show their true derivation. . . . Now the " C.B.H." has come to comprise a hospital of more than sixty beds and, with all its branches, is staffed entirely by Salvation Army officers, of whom all those belonging to the country have received their entire medical or nursing training in The Salvation Army Medical Department itself. . . . As evidence of the degree of success obtained . . . all obtaining the diploma are recognized by the State as competent to enter the Government Medical Service or to have charge of hospitals or dispensaries. . . . The Salvation Army does not favour inferior or incompetent methods in its medical training and practice, for such would be a poor introduction to and recommendation for a Saviour able to save to the uttermost. . . .'[5]

At the close of Turner's stay, in an account of the foundation and development of the hospital, entitled ' The Catherine Booth Hospital for One and Twenty Years ', the following valedictory note is included:

'And now Dr. Turner is leaving India. For twenty-one years he has given of his best to the Catherine Booth Hospital of Nagercoil, and he has his reward. The hospital stands now a monument of God's loving-kindness and power. Spreading from that first small amateur dispensary, it has grown till it covers a vast expanse of land, on which have been erected no less than some score of separate buildings. Said a recent visitor: " I came to see a hospital, I never expected to find a garden city! " It is indeed a wonderful place, wonderful in its surgical and healing work, and wonderful also in its human and missionary element.'

But not the least of Percy Turner's contributions to what had now become a suite of buildings forming a progressive hospital, was his thoroughness and insistence on ' only the best '.

Wrote an officer-colleague: ' His devotion to the highest aims of his profession and calling was most marked. He could not put up with anything that was shoddy or haphazard. He was most careful over details.'

A small notebook, into which Percy Turner copied quotations that appealed to him, includes the following:

' Right, duty, truth, must triumph in the end; but neither one nor the other can triumph unless there are workers in the field who are content to bring all their energies to bear, and who will continue to work, while life is left them, mindful always of others, forgetful always of themselves.'

Dr. Percy Turner's own summing up of the work he and his helpers were seeking to do is found in these words: ' To bring men and women to this Saviour is the supreme end and object of all the work; to heal the sick is indeed in itself a true work of mercy, and one which all the world, Christian and non-Christian, recognizes as worthy of commendation and help; but that which differentiates a missionary hospital from others is the foundation recognition of the fact that the needs of the spirit, wounded by sin and sorrow, are even more important than those of the sick body.'[5]

Returning to England in 1923, Percy Turner served as Chief Medical Officer, International Headquarters, London, until his retirement in 1937 and was responsible for the medical examination of many candidates and the treatment of sick officers. His interest in the welfare of his fellow-men led him, because of his awareness of the need for psychological medicine, to become for a time Clinical Assistant at the Tavistock Clinic, besides serving as a Member of the Society for the Study of Addiction, the Committee of the Medical Missionary Association and the Public Morality Council. He was a Fellow of the Institute of Public Health, a member of the British Medical Association and an Honorary Life Member of the St. John Ambulance Association.

Following his passing, on October 19, 1955, in an obituary notice sent to *The Times*, the *Lancet* and *The British Medical Association*, Mr. A. E. Stevens, F.R.C.S., wrote of him: 'At the commencement of his association with The Salvation Army he experienced much opposition, but he was always convinced he had done the right thing in joining this organization; his faith was simple but inspiring, he was gentle, courteous and kind: a true Christian gentleman in the highest sense of the word.'

Chapter
Three

NOT MERELY
A DOCTOR
CHARLES STEIBEL

BORN in London's West End, Charles Steibel, son of a wealthy Jew, had a privileged start in life. His education was begun at home, under both French and German governesses, before he passed to a series of preparatory schools at Brighton and followed the conventional path through public school (Clifton College) to Cambridge. There, entering Trinity College and ' taking the National Science Tripos, he proceeded to M.B., B.Ch., his medical studies being undertaken at St. Thomas' Hospital, London, where thirty years earlier, Florence Nightingale had commenced the first formal school of nursing '.[6]

When in 1910, as a tall, well-dressed young man, Charles Steibel made his way to The Salvation Army's Regent Hall in

Oxford Street, London, as a week-night meeting was concluding and knelt at the Mercy Seat to pray ' in great agony of soul ', his experience of the world was already considerable. He has been described as ' intelligent, impressionable, quick to love and anger ' and his career had already marked him, even at that time, as highly individualistic. On qualifying he had taken assistantships with general practitioners in Scarborough and in a Cheshire village. ' This taste of responsibility only quickened Steibel's sense of inadequacy ' and he returned to London to take up a then much-coveted appointment as a house surgeon at the West London Hospital, where he spent two years. His reading there included a number of books on Africa, and he conceived a desire to visit it. His father was opposed to the idea but eventually agreed to one year's assistantship to a doctor with an extensive practice at Bethlehem, in the Orange Free State. Charles sailed in April, 1906. ' In excellent health, the open-air life, the rich variety of work and the freedom of colonial society all satisfied him. . . .

' The promised year was up and he had enjoyed a holiday in Basutoland when typhoid fever laid him low. . . . For Steibel this resulted in permanent impairment of digestion and prolonged his stay for six months.' [6]

Following his return to England, the young doctor went first as Assistant Medical Officer to Bradford Infirmary and then to St. Marylebone Infirmary in Notting Hill, the site of which had been earlier selected by the great nursing pioneer herself as having ' maximum air and quiet '. Here Charles was to meet Agatha Cook, who had been a Florence Nightingale probationer and was now Sister-in-charge of male wards. Miss Cook was highly amused when a porter approached her, requesting ' a piece of flannelette for Dr. Steibel to clean his rifle '. ' In such inauspicious ways do romances begin. It took two years to ripen to marriage: in that time Charles found Christ and a life's discipleship. . . . With his conversion, Dr. Steibel, shy though he was, gave witness to his colleagues and patients.' [6]

Early in 1911, with his thoughts now on medical mission, Steibel went first to Moorfields Eye Hospital, London, and then to Newcastle, where he studied surgery before appearing for the F.R.C.S. examination in Edinburgh.

' Evangelicals had opened a series of medical missions in the metropolis. Charles chose one in Islington. . . . Here he came into intimate contact with poverty. This was a period of railway strikes, of hunger and resentment. Charles decided he must live nearer to his people. He cut out evening dinner, had bread and

S

cheese at midday and when his beloved sister, who had also become a Christian, called at his flat in furs she was horrified to find that Charles had dispensed with a coal fire and was huddled in an overcoat. Thus did he prepare himself for service to the poor in India.... Charles and Agatha were married on February 12, 1912, and set out for India the same day.'[6] They were to serve under another Londoner, Dr. Percy Turner, at The Salvation Army's Catherine Booth Hospital, Nagercoil, South India.

On arrival at Salvation Army Headquarters, Bombay, the couple found themselves experiencing for the first time ' how simply and sweetly the Salvation Army officers lived '. There followed a two-day train journey across Central India to Madras, in heat that Agatha found ' prostrating '.

' It is 450 miles from Madras to Nagercoil, but the railway prospectors of the mid-nineteenth century could not obtain permission for the last fifty miles into Kanyakumari (the southernmost district of Travancore).... So the Steibels did as William Booth had done many years before, they travelled from Tirunelvelli by bullock cart.... At breakfast time they crossed the boundary between British India and the Native State of Travancore and saw the first branch of the Catherine Booth Hospital. Aramboly, only eight miles from Nagercoil, was to become familiar.'[6]

When the couple arrived at the Catherine Booth Hospital just before noon, ' Dr. Turner and most of the staff were waiting to give a cordial reception and to escort them to their bungalow, which Charlie promptly named " Blue Bird Cottage ". His eagerness—a boy, despite his thirty-six years—stands out at this point. A wash, a meal, a little rest and at 3 p.m. he was on duty. When he returned to Blue Bird Cottage at 6 p.m. his greeting was, " I've learned some Tamil."

' The Catherine Booth Hospital, to which the Steibels had come, was already fifteen years old and a significant contribution to the medical services of the Travancore State. It was, in fact, the only medical school in the State.

' The medical school was an integral part of the hospital, the students learning as much by an apprenticeship in the wards as by lectures in the classroom. The Steibels' welcome meeting plunged them into the family, for a wedding was included—the bride a nurse, the groom a medical student.

' They tackled every new experience in their own way with Christian love and the best of English courtesy as their tutors.... Soon they settled a routine as a basis for all the extra unexpected

calls that the days brought. . . . Charles finished a night round at
10 p.m. and was up by four, preparing his next lecture for the
students. The hospital day started with prayers at eight, followed
by the lecture . . . ward rounds and then out-patients' clinic, when
quiet spread over Vadasery until 3 p.m., when there was an
operating session, or more out-patients, until 5.30. But Charlie
seldom rested for long: the siesta period was too valuable, for
reading. He read up the operations for that day, or a medical
journal, and indulged in his one relaxation—private reading. . . .
    ' Occasionally there was an anatomy or a pathology lecture in
the evening. Turner and Steibel shared both the teaching and the
surgery, though ophthalmic cases were normally Turner's. Outside
calls were personal. . . . These visits often reduced the hours of
sleep but there was rich reward to the new missionary in insight
into Hindu customs and the entry given to homes and hearts.'[6]
    When cholera struck, demands increased immeasurably.
Christmas Eve, 1912, brought the first of a series of tragic deaths
which marked the beginning of an epidemic that raged throughout Kanyakumari district for six weeks. ' Steibel and Turner
were faced with the dilemma inherent in the situation of all
missionary doctors responsible for a large institution. Can the
hospital be neglected? Is it right to bring virulent infection
within the walls? Turner held his Diploma in Public Health and
weighed the matter judiciously. Steibel was impetuous and new.
They worked out a plan. A breach was made in the compound
wall and, well away from the other wards, a pandal erected,
plaited leaves tied over a bamboo frame. The whole ward was up
in twelve hours. (A succession of such buildings that could be
burned followed.) Charles held a meeting with the thirty medical
students: twelve volunteered and spent all their off-duty in
villages within two miles' radius. They treated patients and saved
some, but even more profitable was their organization of safe
water and control of village practices that spread infection. . . .
For weeks they had little more than three or four hours' sleep.'[6]
    Mrs. Steibel wrote in a personal record published privately in
1920: ' We had no surplus time for such extra duties as were
involved by the cholera epidemic. Charlie had to take it out of his
sleep, and he did it gladly, as the obvious duty of a man who was a
medical missionary and not merely a doctor.'
    After the cholera epidemic Turner suggested a brief holiday,
and Charles and Agatha enjoyed idyllic days at a fishing village on
the coast of the Arabian Sea, a week's journey away by horse and
cart.

Some months of further work in Nagercoil followed before
Charles and Agatha Steibel's services were required in Anand.
They left the Catherine Booth Hospital in ' a cart turned into a
festival chariot with greenery and flowers. All the students were
there . . . singing as they pulled up the hill through Vadasery '.[6]
En route, the couple stayed with Miss Amy Carmichael at
Dohnavur, where 120 little girls were being cared for in the
nursery and day-school. As they had no doctor, Charlie held a
clinic and did some smallpox vaccinations. ' They left Dohnavur
by bullock bandy as night fell . . . arriving at the railway station by
sunrise. Four hundred miles to Madras, another 800 to Bombay,
and they still had the 260 miles to Anand.'[6]

The missionary sister preparing breakfast for the new arrivals
noted with joy that the doctor and his wife took time to pray in
their bedroom before appearing for the meal. ' I was overjoyed,'
she wrote, ' feeling that a man after God's own heart had come
amongst us. At that breakfast, first of many meals together, I was
touched by his humility and brotherly kindness.'

' Consistent with his Nagercoil record, Charlie was over at the
Emery Hospital by 8 a.m. and had his first operation list that
same afternoon! Agatha left her unpacking and acted as theatre
sister. . . . There had been no missionary doctor for some time and
Charles accepted a waiting list of surgical cases. . . .

' The district soon took notice of the new doctor. It was
quoted in the bazaar that he would answer village calls whenever
possible, took no notice of fees and never wasted time. . . . He
prayed earnestly before surgery, and . . . lived up to his prayers in his
concern for individual patients. . . . The richer patients found him in-
corruptible and were amazed at his devotion to destitute patients.'[6]

Charles' tenderness extended also to the animals which surrounded his new home. ' Little grey squirrels shared the trees
with the monkeys and crows. At their chirrup he would look up
from his early morning Bible-reading to see them washing themselves like kittens. He would coax them on to the verandah while
having *al fresco* breakfast, dropping toast to bring them even
nearer. One made a nest in a pair of socks and Charles reared the
babies with a fountain pen filler.'[6]

With the outbreak of the First World War, Dr. Steibel felt he
must volunteer for the Indian Medical Service. His term of
service with The Salvation Army was nearly up and a brief period
of indecision was followed by the dispatch of a letter to Salvation
Army headquarters in Simla, indicating his determination to
proceed on military service.

It was typical of the man that, like Dr. Harry Andrews, who was to win the V.C. posthumously for his service to wounded Indian soldiers, Charles Steibel also should give his life while picking up wounded Indian troops—the latter before the front-line trenches near Kut, in Mesopotamia, on February 2, 1917. By this time he had two baby girls, the first daughter named after her mother—and born in Brighton, England, where No. 1. Indian General Hospital was located—and another born in 1916 and named after his sister, Evelyn.

News of Charles Steibel's death brought sorrow to his Salvationist colleagues in India, many of whom, with Charles himself, had hoped that a return to his old work might become possible with a cessation of hostilities. 'It would be nice to see Blue Bird Bungalow again,' he had written. 'But we must not let the attractive point the way to duty. I do so want to be a soldier of God's.'

Writing of the two men, Harry Andrews and Charles Steibel, Lieut.-Commissioner (Dr.) Harry Williams, successor to them both, at Anand and at Nagercoil, has said, 'I have trod all the country Charles Steibel knew in India and, like Harry Andrews, I was a Captain in the Indian Medical Service (when the Thomas Emery Hospital in Moradabad became a base hospital for Indian casualties in the Second World War). Sometimes, contemplating their portraits, I have wondered why Andrews (posthumously) received the V.C. and Steibel's widow only a letter from his Colonel. Their exploits were similar. I have an idea that their character and their impress upon their contemporaries may have had something to do with it.'

Charles Steibel was inherently a shy man—he has been described as 'six foot of gentleman'—whereas Harry Andrews, a small man, was a veritable dynamo among men. 'He was a man of commanding personality,' writes Harry Williams of Andrews, 'and had the Booth "drive", but showed such tenderness and selflessness towards his patients that they worshipped him.' This was obviously true of both men.

> . . . Their work continueth,
> Broad and deep continueth,
> Greater than their knowing.

SIGHT FOR
THE BLIND
VILHELM WILLE

Chapter

Four

' Go to Dr. Wille: he will help you if anybody can.' The blind man, given this advice and taking his place in the line of Javanese patients outside the low barrack, with walls of plaited bamboo, was one of a long queue waiting for attention to their eyes, affected by many conditions from mild trachoma to total blindness. The year could be between 1908 and 1914, the place a permanent beggars' colony in the island of Java, where since 1905 The Salvation Army has cared for the sick and destitute, first brought together in an old prison at Bugangan, near Semarang, following a flood disaster.

Captain (Dr.) and Mrs. Vilhelm Wille had arrived at the colony in 1907 from their native Denmark. The doctor had left a flourishing practice and a high reputation as an obstetrician and eye specialist in Køge, where he had practised since 1892, to devote himself to the life of a Salvationist medical missionary.

Even before they became Salvationists, the doctor and his wife had a reputation for good works. They held evangelical meetings in their home, and the doctor would pray with his patients and witness to his Christian faith. He was called ' the holy doctor ', though soon without irony, and was known to be a friend of the poor. His devoted care for drunkards and deep personal involvement with them became a byword. It was little wonder that, when The Salvation Army appeared on the scene, the doctor and his wife were attracted. In April 1905, they became Salvationists and were soon active. Uniform-wearing was no difficulty to the good doctor, in fact, quite the opposite. When told by the Salvation Army headquarters that it was unnecessary for him to wear uniform constantly he replied that with God's help he would be continuing to wear it, and if patients did not care for it they would have to tolerate it. However, there was no slackening in the number of his patients, and the poor and destitute were often taken into his home.

In February 1906, Bramwell Booth was in Copenhagen and Dr. and Mrs. Wille heard his call for candidates for the overseas field. The couple's decision was prompt and thoroughgoing. If Christ's call was, ' Go, sell what you possess and give to the poor . . . and come follow Me ', they would do just that. They were ready to go the whole way. A journey to England, five months' training there and their appointment to Java followed. They travelled East with four young children. The doctor was ready for anything and Bugangan needed him. The first operation would, he knew, be critical in winning the confidence of the people, especially as local priests, hearing of his coming, had warned the people against receiving treatment from a European. With much prayer the important first eye-surgery took place. The patient was a sightless Chinese. When the surgical intervention proved a success, prejudice against the doctor began to break down.

An appalling amount of sickness and suffering soon confronted him. ' The overcrowded Semarang hospitals were sending to the Army's colony their cases of skin and venereal disease. Many were also stricken with trachoma and other eye troubles; not a few had lost their sight. The Danish doctor's specialized knowledge in this field found ample scope and the healing marvels wrought on these unfortunates, regarded by many as worthless, spread his fame far and wide.'[7]

But it was not local fame that was the attraction for Vilhelm Wille. Later, in a letter home, he wrote: ' In spite of much work, I am grateful and happy about my position, as *I can use all my time and strength in the work for Jesus, and in a manner that so reminds me of His own.*' Mrs. Wille was equally enthusiastic. ' I think it is the most glorious position in the world,' she wrote ' to be a Salvation Army officer.'[8]

' The number of consultations rose by leaps and bounds, from about 7,000 in 1908 to 24,000 in 1909 and 41,000 in 1913. More than 5,000 eye patients were treated in those six years, and not far from half of the 2,705 eye operations performed were of a serious character.'[7]

European patients by this time were eagerly seeking the good doctor's help, but ' if some well-to-do business man, who paid full fees, complained that he was not given preference over some poor person the doctor would courteously reply: " Sir, I quite understand. But you, too, must understand. You are able to pay any of the medical men practising on the island, while these (with a gesture towards the miserable beggars and others) have no one else to whom they can go. I shall be happy to do my best for you—if you will be good enough to await your turn ".'[7]

His reputation spread. Patients of many races arrived for treatment. One day Dr. Wille treated a life-prisoner—a man with an iron ring round his neck, convicted of murder—followed by

some poor Javanese and then the daughter of a Dutch Admiral.
A blind couple, led by their five-year-old son, had walked for
eight days to reach Bugangan. Too late to be helped, because
they had not been brought for treatment in time, they left the
same way. A blind girl, bidden in a dream to go eastward, arrived
seeking help, was healed under the doctor's care and became a
Christian.[8]

'The bearded Salvationist's bright smile was disarming and
he was, after all, Dr. Wille. Even wealthy patients stood in awe
of such a man's devotion and self-abnegation. It was no secret
that the allowance he, like other Salvation Army officers, received
was only a fraction of what he could have earned with far less toil
than his present work demanded.

'Mrs. Wille took a large part in her husband's work. For a
couple of years she was his only assistant (later their daughter
Elizabeth . . . rendered valuable help).'[7] Even later, when
Javanese helpers were available, Mrs. Wille continued to share in
bandaging and nursing her husband's patients. She learned also
independently to treat minor trachoma cases.

At first the doctor had been hampered by the law which
required a Dutch diploma before anyone could practise—at least
on Europeans—in what was then a Dutch Colony. For lack of
this, even his prescriptions could not be made up by chemists in
Java. He had to prepare for an examination by a Dutch medical
board. By the sixth and last day of the examination the board's
surprise at the ability and knowledge of the slight, bearded
Dane, in Salvationist uniform, had given place to unqualified
admiration.

Later his diagnosis—published in the leading medical journal
—of an eye-disease very prevalent in the East, which had robbed
thousands—especially children—of their sight, established his
already growing reputation. 'Wille knew the disease from
isolated occurrences in his own country, and he was the first in
Indonesia to describe it as xerophthalmia caused by avitaminosis
—deficient nourishment. He achieved notable cures by a diet of
milk, eggs, liver, cod-liver oil, etc.'[7]

(Contributions to medical journals went on, even after retirement. The International Index-Catalogue shows articles were
published in 1921, 1927 and each year from 1933–38.)[8]

But the work in the beginning was not done without cost in
personal suffering. Before his first homeland furlough in 1913
the doctor and his children had all suffered from dysentry,
malaria and typhus. (Cholera was an unwelcome visitor to

Semarang in 1909.) In 1908 the parents lost their bonny second daughter, nine-year-old Andrea Vilhelmina from dysentry.

With unabated zeal the doctor and his wife gave themselves not only to medical work but to the preaching of the gospel, particularly when they had achieved some mastery of the language. Beside taking part in indoor gatherings, they held open-air services, and Dr. Wille also spoke in prison meetings. Mrs. Wille visited the huts of the patients with song, guitar and prayer. Sariem, a blind Christian girl, helped Mrs. Wille with translation as it was needed. Out of their own savings the couple printed a pamphlet specially directed to Muslims.

The need for larger accommodation for the medical work became pressing. An eye hospital was planned and the Territorial Commander, assisted by the good doctor, did some successful collecting.

When, in 1915, a newly-erected eye hospital was opened on the hilly outskirts of Semarang, with the help of £2,500 collected from wealthy business men of prominent firms and a Government grant of double that amount, the doctor and his wife felt they had at last acquired convenient surroundings in which to treat the many who were now seeking help. What a joy it was to have proper working rooms, consultation and examination rooms—in place of the plaited straw-walled dark room—an up-to-date operating theatre, sterilizing instruments, a dispensing room, a laboratory and an office! ' There were proper quarters for sisters and nurses, wards for paying patients and free wards for over ninety men, women and children.

' While Mrs. Wille and, at intervals, an assistant doctor, together with the nurses, attended to the many patients' treatment, Dr. Wille himself saw to the examinations and operations. The latter took up three mornings a week from 8 a.m. to 1.30 p.m., with a quarter of an hour's break for " coffee ", but [appreciated] even more for private devotions. From 4 p.m. to 8 p.m. he was available for further consultations; then, when a second shift of nurses came on duty, the doctor had a cup of coffee and went on working—for some years often till midnight.'[7]

A press representative of one of Java's most widely read newspapers wrote: ' I greatly admire this man. What enthusiasm, what self-effacement, what immovable faith, what trust in God, what love, what self-sacrifice! '[8]

In 1920 Dr. Wille's name was in the first list of admissions to the newly-created Order of the Founder, The Salvation Army's supreme recognition of outstanding service, such as would have

commended itself to William Booth. The citation reads: ' Major
(Dr.) Vilhelm Wille: for self-denying and quite exceptional
labours in pioneering and leading the important work of the
Army on behalf of the blind in Indonesia.'

The following year Queen Wilhelmina of the Netherlands
appointed him an Officer of the Dutch Order of Oranje-Nassau;
and in 1937 King Christian X of Denmark made him a Knight
of his native land's Dannebrog Order.

' In 1931 Lieut.-Colonel Dr. Wille retired from the charge of
the Semarang Hospital, maintaining a private practice in that
town and, later, in Bandung. Still his favourite patients were his
old Salvation Army comrades and " society's step-children ".
He continued scientific studies, and as late as 1938 had a paper
published in the *British Journal of Ophthalmology.*

' He retained, too, his love of evangelistic work, and Sunday
after Sunday the famous surgeon would take part in the Army's
open-air meetings, witnessing to large gatherings of Javanese,
Chinese and others, of Christ's redemptive power—right to the
day when the occupation forces stopped the Salvationists' public
activities.'[7]

Following the rather sudden death of his wife in 1925 after
an operation, Vilhelm Wille had in 1928 married Ensign Ellen
Erle, a Salvation Army nurse, who in his last illness cared for him
with loving devotion. Serene and secure in a child-like faith,
Vilhelm Andreas Wille went to his eternal reward on May 24,
1944.

His life-span (1862 to 1944) had seen the introduction of
antiseptic surgery in Copenhagen, where he had himself operated
one of the carbolic sprays invented by Lister, and ultimately the
emergence of penicillin as another history-making weapon with
which to fight infection.

Salvation Army medical work still continues in Java (now
Djawa) as well as in Celebes (Sulawesi); and hospitals at Semarang,
Surabaja and Turen maintain service to the varied peoples among
whom Dr. Wille rendered such selfless pioneering service.

CALLED TO LIVE FOR THE POOR
SANYA MATSUDA

Chapter

Five

' CHRISTLIKE Matsuda '—this was the highly significant name by which his Japanese Salvationist comrades recalled their saintly doctor-friend and colleague who, in 1930, died of tuberculosis, the disease he had dedicated his life to fighting as a young man among them, many years earlier.

Dr. Sanya Matsuda was awarded The Salvation Army's highest honour—the Order of the Founder—in 1924, ' for patient and self-sacrificing service among the sick and suffering, and especially for his devoted labours at The Salvation Army's Sanatorium at Tokyo (Japan) '.

As a medical student, Dr. Matsuda was influenced by the Salvationist witness of Dr. Wakiya, who then held the position of Treasurer at Hongo Corps. William Booth's visit to Japan in 1907 made an indelible impression upon Matsuda. He found his Christian faith stimulated and challenged. Later the doctor ' sought out the aged warrior and hung upon his words.'[9]

One of William Booth's impassioned pleas at that time was for the care of the very poor sick. (He had learned of their sufferings from his officers in Tokyo, who had told him of the many who died unattended by any medical practitioner, for want of the fees to pay for their help.) William Booth proposed a free hospital for the needy sick. When the Founder died in 1912, therefore, it was felt that a fitting memorial to him in Japan would be just such a hospital. Donations poured in from rich and poor alike, for William Booth's visit had made a profound impression on the Japanese people. (' If this man remains long in Japan,' a newspaper had commented, ' he will change its religion, for he speaks not as the professors, but as a man with a soul in possession of secrets.'[10]) The royal family's donation was one of the halls which had been especially built earlier to accommodate visitors to a royal funeral. It was to become the main reception hall of the new healing centre for the poor.

As the hospital began to take shape the question arose as to where a qualified medical man could be found to superintend its healing ministry. Lieut.-Colonel Gunpei Yamamuro, Japanese-born Chief Secretary of the Army's work in Japan, appealed publicly for a candidate to fill the vacant post. Who would

respond? In this connection he made a special personal approach
to one he felt would suitably carry the dual Christian and medical
responsibility.

The Japanese medical world was stirred by the response of
Dr. Sanya Matsuda. His large practice and highly paid position—
he was a lecturer much in demand—were to be sacrificed for an
opportunity to minister to the sick poor of Tokyo. Those who
knew him, however, felt that his offer was in character with their
colleague's avowed Christian profession. Some had heard him
stress the value of Christian commitment in a life of medical
service. He had often referred to David Livingstone as a pattern.
'But you need not go to Africa,' Dr. Matsuda had said; 'here in
your own city of Tokyo there are slums of utter darkness and
misery.'

A visitor to Japan in succeeding years described how she had
accompanied Dr. Matsuda and his helpers—Dr. Iwasa and Nurse
Kamada—on one of his rounds of visitation to the sick in their
homes.[11] 'We took the tram (half an hour's ride) to Hinji. At
first the houses seemed ordinary one-storey dwellings, but turning
a corner we came to what looked like the entrance to a house, a
very poor one. The doctors and nurse disappeared and, being
called to follow, I found myself in a long, narrow, dark, earthen
floor passage, with doors at close intervals on either side leading
into small rooms. These dwellings . . . are . . . large, hastily built
low-roofed sheds, a passage running down the centre of each,
rooms on either side, a family in each room. . . . Drainage and
sanitary arrangements generally were non-existent. In the rainy
season, when everything mildews, and again in the summer,
when the sun's hot rays are beating down, life must become truly
unbearable.'

The writer describes the old, torn wall-paper in the first room,
the discoloured matting on the floor, and the paper windows,
torn and smoked. Two small children were alone in the room,
an empty rice pan before them from which they had evidently
just finished their meal.

In the second room was a sick baby, a mother bending over
it and a little girl about three years of age at her side. The doctor,
'his tall form looking taller still beneath the low ceiling', stepped
over to where the baby was, and knelt on a cushion beside it.
The child was suffering from bronchitis.

In the next room, where a blind woman of sixty-eight awaits
the doctor, a small child 'about six, who has a very bad trachoma
eye' comes to join the woman; 'his father is away at work'.

Another room is occupied by a mother, her crippled son and little daughter four years old. (The father, who had died, had been one of the doctor's patients.)

'None of them looks very robust,' comments the visitor. '[The mother] asks me if the doctor will examine her chest. He does. She is consumptive.'

Meantime, in the hospital itself, work is proceeding, and during the course of the slum visitation a message arrives for Dr. Matsuda. Two professors with fifty students from Waseda University (Count Okuma's) have called to inspect the hospital. Of course the doctor must return.

When the visitor to Japan later asked, ' What led you to become a Christian and a Salvationist, doctor?', this was Dr. Matsuda's reply:

' It was at Doshisha College, Kyoto, where I went when I was sixteen years of age, that I first heard about Christianity.

' When eighteen I came to Tokyo, intending to study medicine, and for this purpose entered the Dai I Koto Gakko, and later the Imperial University, where I took my degree. Previous to this I was baptised as a Christian . . . and, as I wished to be a Christian doctor, entered Dr. Takata's hospital. [Dr. Takata, a Christian, had charge of one of the largest hospitals in Japan for tuberculosis sufferers at the time.]

' From the very first . . . I felt called to live especially for the poor and needy. During the Russo-Japanese War, as doctor-in-charge of the American Red Cross nurses' party, I gained some experience of the military hospital system, and I felt that if I was to do anything effective for the poor it must be by adopting the military system plus the Christian system!

' There was The Salvation Army, so I began to study it—I'd known Yamamuro San* from student days, and was in Tokyo when the Army commenced its work. . . . Then, when the late General visited Japan, I heard him speak of his hospital scheme. The hospital was being erected when, at the 1912 New Year celebrations, I was enrolled as a Salvationist.

' Shortly after this I was asked to accept the position of Superintendent of the hospital and I gladly consented. Indeed, in doing so I seemed to be reaching the ideal of my life, and felt I was receiving the answer to all my prayers and the fulfilment of my desires.'[11]

Obviously Dr. Matsuda's enthusiasm was no passing youthful fancy. The years attested its purity and lasting quality.

* The Chief Secretary, later Territorial Commander, already mentioned.

SHE EASED THE WAY
FOR OTHERS

Chapter

Six

RIN IWASA

WHEN, on the first day of January 1891, a baby girl was born into the home of an aristocratic Japanese family, The Salvation Army had been at work in Japan only four years. The child, Rin Iwasa, third daughter among seven, was one of eleven children. Their father, ' a peace-loving, high principled gentleman, with a reputation extending far beyond his native city of Nagoya ',[9] was determined that each of his children should receive the highest education available.

' Rin, tall, slim and attractive ... proved brilliant intellectually, graduating as early as fifteen years of age. ... An infectious gaiety of spirit made her popular—[she] excelled in Japanese folk-dancing and played well above the average in sports but an intensity of purpose shone through all she did.

' Tokyo Medical School was then in its infancy. The young girl's decision to enter it as a student had been formed largely through reading about Florence Nightingale. ... She desired nothing better herself than a like task in her own land. ... On the threshold of preparation for life, she contacted a spirit matching her own.'[9]

Among the professors serving the medical school was Dr. Sanya Matsuda. In his lectures he was emphatic about the paramount importance of character in medical men and women. Above all, he told his students, the best equipment for their career could be gained through a personal knowledge of Jesus Christ. His own Christlike character was a silent testimony to the truth of his words. A modest man by temperament, he was a fearless challenger as a Salvationist, and his words found their mark.

' This one Christian among their thirty instructors seemed to her a noble personality, whose counsel she could completely trust. Other students felt Dr. Matsuda's impact and were roused to seek true values. Led by Rin, about a third of her class-mates would troop out to visit the Salvationist in his modest home.

' The medical staff of the college saw all this with distaste; they were far from favouring the students' attendance at Christian gatherings. Instinctively realizing their attitude, Rin would sometimes stay in the school dormitory, where she would read books which gave her a wide knowledge of The Salvation Army and of Christianity itself, for all was new to the young girl who had been brought up carefully in the Buddhist-Shintoist philosophy of her parents.

'Two months after she had taken her degree, the new young doctor's mind was made up. She would join Matsuda's staff; she would take life on the same terms as he.'[9]

There followed a visit to her home, to face her parents on the issue. A 'bitter battle' ensued which led to two months of what the young woman referred to as 'days of agony'. Her father was set on her returning to Nagoya and forming a medical practice among his affluent Buddhist friends. Eventually she won his consent to go back to the capital, but only temporarily and to 'study the poor'. On no account was she to become a Salvationist.

The cherished ideals which had led to this family conflict were to be put to some severe tests. The young doctor discovered that the staff of the new hospital actually went out to find and bring back the sick poor from the slums where they lived, and where 'conditions were offensive to every natural instinct of a young woman reared in seclusion and comfort'.[9]

At the hospital an epidemic of measles called for heroism in an alarming situation. 'Two desperate mothers arrived, with suffering mites strapped to their backs. One baby was found to have died on the way, the other was critically ill. Dr. Iwasa went out . . . to see for herself the conditions in which they suffered. She found a hovel without any window sheltering eighteen people, all seriously ill. She had to examine them by flashlamp, though outside was broad daylight. None had been able to pay for medical help. The mother of the dead baby had lost four children there already. In another barrack type of building sixty-one families were discovered in hopeless misery. Compassionately Rin, with her young nurses, tended them and promised help.

'When the Army's small general hospital could cope no longer, it was resolved to build and open a tuberculosis sanatorium. This also would be unique, as the first devoted solely to patients unable to pay.'[9]

The next significant milestone in Dr. Iwasa's life was when she travelled to London, with a representative Japanese group, to attend the fourth Salvation Army International Congress, held in June 1914. At one time during the voyage she became aware of 'a heavenly direction for her surrendered life' and when the great gathering closed, while the party returned to Japan, she remained in London for training as a Salvation Army officer. Commissioned as a Captain in 1915, she was appointed to Japan, and returned from war-torn Europe to face a fresh crisis with her parents when they learned of the new responsibilities she was to take up in the sanatorium. Alarm over the risk to their daughter's health was added to the hostility they already felt.

'An inner assurance of being in her God-ordained place supported her.' Nevertheless for five troubled years she was beset by calls, letters and telegrams urging a return home. 'As they themselves admitted, the same heroic service done by a stranger would have had their admiration; in their daughter it could not be tolerated! '[9]

Accepting the personal sorrow of her parents' disapproval, the young woman—who has been described as ' physically lovely to look at '—reflected in her face a calm peace and always had an encouraging smile for those with whom she worked. Later her sorrow was to be turned into joy by her parents' whole-hearted approval of their daughter's choice of this life-course; but meantime in spirit she often walked alone.

This did not mean that she was in any sense self-centred, however, and her wise counsel made light of many problems. ' When I knew her,' an officer-wife later related, ' it was early days in Japan for women to enter public life. She must have been one of the first doctors. She made it easier for Japanese girls to start working as doctors and nurses.'

Dr. Rin Iwasa became ' Dr. Matsuda's right-hand-man. About two hundred poor patients were under her care, and fifty staff took her directions. Their . . . co-operation with Matsuda won fame for the sanatorium ',[9] and it became known as a model of its kind.

When, in 1930, The Salvation Army in Japan suffered the loss of its foremost physician, Christlike Dr. Matsuda, the question of who could follow him as Superintendent called for an answer. It was extraordinary in Japan at that time for a woman to be given such a responsibility, ' but there could only be one name in answer to the question—Dr. Rin Iwasa '. Like her esteemed predecessor, she had been earlier awarded the Army's highest honour. The citation accompanying the award to Adjutant (later Lieut.-Colonel) (Dr.) Rin Iwasa described it as being ' for compassionate and devoted toil amongst sufferers from tuberculosis in Japan, and in the establishment of a sanatorium in Tokyo '.

Courageously the woman officer-doctor faced her heavier responsibility, now that the mantle of her former director had fallen on her, carrying on many new ideas which Matsuda had discussed with her and begun to introduce. Plans for yet another sanatorium had been envisaged. This next life-saving venture was started in the spring of 1939, when the approach of another world war was already throwing its long shadow ahead. Heartbreaks and ' teething problems ' were not spared Rin Iwasa as the full impact of war conditions fell on Japan itself, and ultimately upon the western-originated Army. Though both sanatoria were taken over by the Government, their woman Superintendent was ordered to continue as chief medical officer, in charge of over four hundred patients, and one hundred employees.

' For her contribution to social welfare work the doctor received the Emperor's Order of the Blue Ribbon in 1944. . . . The Salvation Army in Japan was publicly honoured when in 1946 Lieut.-Colonel (Dr.) Rin Iwasa received a summons to lecture the Emperor and Empress on tuberculosis work.'

Pursuing her indefatigable labours, the doctor was frequently caught up in service to the needy on a large scale as when, in April 1948, she was in the thick of a great relief operation, giving treatment herself to victims of a flood which devastated huge areas of the Kwanto plain on the outskirts of Tokyo. Even after ill health had caused her retirement from the public scene, like her ideal heroine—Florence Nightingale—before her, she conducted business affairs (concerning the great sanatoria) from her bed.

Though announcements of Dr. Iwasa's promotion to Glory included one headed 'A remarkable life closed ', obviously there can be no close to the influence of such a life. The official Salvation Army Year Book record of the event, though economically worded, has significant overtones for those who know the Rin Iwasa story:

Lt.-Col. (Dr.) RIN IWASA, O.F.—Out of Tokyo Hospital, 1914, Superintendent Kiyose and Suginami T.B. Sanatoria.
(From Suginami, June 19, 1949.)

Chapter
Seven

HE GAVE ALL
HE HAD
ARTHUR SWAIN

AMONG the non-Salvationist doctors who have given sterling service to The Salvation Army's medical missionary field was

Dr. Arthur Swain, a member of the Plymouth Brethren, whose aggressive evangelism had already made its mark when he served with the British Army in the First World War. With men of a like outlook he had taken a keen part in evangelical open-air meetings. That his devotion to God had been well marked by others was evident one day from the rather caustic question of the Regimental Sergeant-Major, who was not altogether satisfied with his military bearing or precision. ' Swain, thinking more of your God than of your King? ' he asked acidly.

But Swain was not one to be deflected from a chosen course, and his loyalty was irrevocably given to his heavenly Guide and Captain. It was this loyalty that caused him to sign for life-service with The Salvation Army, even though he may have found some of its methods somewhat daunting. It is recorded that one of his first contacts with Salvationists *en masse*, soon after being accepted as the prospective doctor-in-charge of a hospital being planned in North China, was at the Crystal Palace, London. The experience so overwhelmed him that he quickly left the scene and hurried home!

It was in the 1920's that Dr. Swain first arrived in China to become himself involved in the planning of the new hospital to be set up at Ting Hsien, Hopei. The disturbed conditions of the area, however, made it impossible for plans to reach completion and, in 1927, arrangements were made for his transfer to the Salvation Army Hospital in Anand, Gujerat, Western India, where as Superintendent his energies were soon fully occupied, to the exclusion of dwelling too deeply on disappointed hopes for a life-work in China.

With unflagging energy he applied himself to the daily routine at Anand. Out-patients were all seen before lunch, even if it meant postponing the meal for an hour or two. After lunch, refusing the usual siesta period when it was customary for Europeans to relax, Dr. Swain would return to the hospital for a busy session of surgery, continued until every scheduled operation had been completed, even if he worked until ten o'clock at night.

One particular personal problem challenged the doctor during his period at Anand. He had quite a number of Salvation Army officers working under his direction at the hospital, all of whom he recognized were non-smokers. The same was true of the majority of Salvationist employees there. The doctor himself smoked a pipe. 'As Superintendent of this hospital should I not be an example as well as a chief? ' he asked himself, and with the inevitable result that he surrendered the comfort of his pipe, though some remember that for a time he could be seen going his rounds with fountain pen in mouth!

Recall to China, and the Superintendency of the modern hospital which had meanwhile been practically completed, gave Arthur Swain real joy. A description of the hospital, erected to cater for 800 villages, is contained in a book about Mary Layton,[12] a dedicated nurse who arrived to be Dr. Swain's untiring helper at Ting Hsien. The year was 1932. 'At last the place came into view—an imposing set of one-storey buildings grouped in several acres of ground and surrounded by a white wall.

' Specially planned to help the country people, the hospital was a mile-and-a-half from the nearest railway station and large town. Built around a great square, the administration block included officers' quarters, waiting-rooms, dispensary, out-patients' department, laboratory, sterilizing and anaesthetic rooms, theatres, private wards, kitchen and laundry. From this block long corridors led to two wards, each of which contained twenty-six beds. A further sixteen beds were in the sanatorium, a separate building with a large glass sun-room.

'Around the hospital, but also within the white walls, were various other necessary buildings, some in course of erection— the doctor's residence, the nurses' quarters, coolies' quarters, a watchman's lodge, mortuary and garage, while above all, and eloquent of the dangers of the land, was the watch-tower. A splendid group of buildings they looked. . . .

' For some months the doctor had been in residence, person-ally supervising the making of furniture and installation of other equipment. Timber, at his request, had been sent up by river-boat, and carpenters had built to his specification on the spot. The wards . . . were airy and bright, with many large windows and doors, and with gaily-coloured quilts on the beds. . . . In the centre of the ward was the nurses' table, with chair and dressing trolley.

' " The wards are a fine width and can be used for assembly purposes," explained the doctor. . . . " I thought perhaps the Sunday morning meeting might be held in one ward, and the Sunday evening in the other. That would give every patient a chance of hearing the gospel." '

The hospital was registered as a training school for nurses in midwifery, general and T.B. nursing. With competent assistance, the devoted doctor threw himself more fully than ever into service for the needy who crowded to it for help.

Almost three years after Dr. Swain had welcomed Captain

Mary Layton, *The Crusader*, an English supplement to the Chinese equivalent of *The War Cry* published in Peking, bore the significant announcements: 'It is with deep regret that Dr. Swain, who has been in charge of the Ting Hsien Hospital since the opening, has been compelled, by doctor's orders, to take three months' complete rest at the Western Hills. . . . It is pleasing to report that Captain (Nurse) Layton after her recent operation is in good health and spirits.'

That the doctor had been driving himself against increasing weariness had been obvious for some time to those closest to him, but his spirit was always keen to triumph over bodily weakness, as was evident in a chorus published in the preceding issue of *The Crusader*, and which he had written while fighting encroaching illness:

> For grace to keep on, Lord,
> For grace I pray;
> Though Satan waylay me,
> My own flesh betray me,
> Give grace to keep on, Lord,
> Through each passing day.

For a time the doctor seemed to benefit from his rest. Hospital affairs were managed by others, doing their best under the circumstances. The November issue of *The Crusader* announced, however, that the doctor and his family would be returning to England. Arrangements were being made for their departure that month.

'Doctor Swain, by his devotion, self sacrifice and unceasing toil has endeared himself to all who have come into contact with him, and his service in and for China will not soon be forgotten,' said the report. 'His skill in his profession, united with a tender nature and unfailing patience and courtesy, have set up a standard to which it will not be easy for all to attain. . . . Our sympathy goes out to Mrs. Swain, who has nobly stood by her husband in all the varying episodes of his work.'

A small and sorrowful party gathered at the Chien Men Station in Peking to bid Dr. Swain and his wife farewell. Two or three seats had been reserved so that the doctor could lie down on the long journey to the coast. In an autograph book presented to him before the train left, he inscribed words from a well-loved song:

> I take, O Cross, thy shadow
> For my abiding place;
> I ask no other sunshine than
> The sunshine of His face.

An officer later recalled, ' We hardly knew how to say good-bye. He could not lean out of the carriage window to be prayed for and sent off with a song ', as was customary when a comrade left for his homeland. The leader responsible for the send-off felt it was providential that the Mayor of Peking happened to be travelling by the same train and a Chinese brass band was filling the air with sound. The little group of unusually silent Salvationists prayed the doctor off in their hearts as the train began its long journey.

Embarking on the s.s. *Rawalpindi*, the ailing doctor had contact on the way home with Salvation Army leaders who met and shared Christian fellowship with him in his time of need. With Herbert Lord in Singapore he conversed at deep level and they each expressed the confidence that God is not inconsistent, both revealing the kind of trust that is the only assurance of peace in pressing need. Arriving in Colombo, the doctor testified to Henry Bowyer that the conversations in Singapore had been a means of real stimulus and cheer to him.

Within four days of arrival in England Arthur Swain had gone to be with his Lord.

' He gave all he had. That summed up the life and work of Dr. Swain,' an officer wrote from China. ' He allowed no consideration for health or personal welfare to deflect him from his chosen course. Those of us who worked by his side marvelled to see how he fought against rapidly increasing physical weakness. We felt he should have given up long before he did, but he insisted on attending to his patients until the last day he was at the hospital. He was carried along by a great devotion to the Chinese.'

Chinese members of the hospital staff, writing to Mrs. Swain after the doctor's passing, said they felt he had deliberately sacrificed his life for the work's sake.

' I have never met a man who spent himself and his means more zealously for his Master,' wrote another officer, whose responsibilities had brought him into close touch with aspects of the doctor's personal giving to God. ' The doctor not only believed in consistent giving to the Lord's work,' he wrote, ' but he insisted on it being done anonymously. One plan was that a certain month in every year the whole month's salary was to be devoted to the work of the Lord, and as that month drew near I would receive a confidential letter from the doctor, asking for advice about to what use this special offering was to be put.

' This was by no means the full extent of his giving, for each month witnessed a setting aside of the Lord's portion to be distributed when and where it was required.'

When, on one occasion, surprise was expressed to the doctor about a man he had helped rather liberally and who seemed to be a somewhat unworthy object for his aid, Arthur Swain's reply was typical of his generous and trustful spirit: ' It may be that I shall never see the man again, and it is possible that he will " make good ".'

The same issue of *The Crusader* which carried these tributes to the devoted doctor also held the brief announcement: ' Several of the nurses attached to the Army General Hospital at Ting Hsien, Hopei, have successfully graduated. Congratulations are offered on the work of Captain Mary Layton and the late medical Superintendent, Dr. Arthur Swain.'

PART TWO

Following the Trail

THE work of Salvation Army medical missionary pioneers can be said to cover, roughly, the period between 1900 and 1930, after which arose what might be termed ' the second generation ', those who followed on, though some served also with the pioneers. The later group—a company of men and women no whit less dedicated—faced a task usually different from that of their predecessors. While some of them were certainly trail-blazers too, others shouldered responsibility for building on the foundations of those who had served before them or deciding when, and in what direction, new extensions or modifications of the earlier work were necessary. All have known the everyday stresses and demands of medical missionary service and have frequently been faced with less than adequate resources of men, money or materials. Some have served for longer and some for shorter periods than those who went before.

The names of the doctors of ' the second generation ', whose stories appear in the chapters of this part, became familiar to Salvationists through Salvation Army publications and by other means.

Others who have given valued service include:

Dr. Samuel Burfoot. Thos. Emery Hospital, Moradabad, 1911; Muktipur Dispensary 1916; Chini Dispensary 1916; Dohad Dispensary 1918; M.O., MacRobert Hospital, Dhariwal, N.E. India, 1923; C.M.O., 1932.

Dr. Edward Barnett. M.O., Thos. Emery Hospital, Moradabad, 1932–36.

Dr. Edgar Stevens. M.O., Thos. Emery Hospital, Moradabad, 1936; Military service with I.M.S. from 1941.

Dr. Reg. Neeve. M.O., Emery Hospital, Anand, W. India, 1938; Military service with I.M.S. from 1941; C.M.O., Thos. Emery Hospital, Moradabad, 1948–52.

Dr. Kingsley Mortimer and Mrs. (Dr.) Mavis Mortimer (*née* McKenzie). M.O., 1944–46; C.M.O. 1946–47, Chikankata; A.M.O., Catherine Booth Hospital, Nagercoil, 1950; C.M.O., Wm. Booth Hospital, Surabaja, Indonesia, 1955–57.

Dr. Eileen Mackintosh (*née* Stanford). Sister-in-Charge, Howard, Rhodesia, 1944–47; M.O., Kolanya, (Kenya) 1956–58; M.O., Nidubrolu Hospital, Madras and Andhra, (India), 1959–61; M.O. i/c, Howard Hospital, Rhodesia, 1963–65.

Dr. Stanley Pearson. M.O., Nidubrolu Hospital, Madras and Andhra (India) 1946–50; Anand, Western India, 1950–51.

Dr. Gunther S. Gramsch. M.O., Thos. Emery Hospital, Moradabad, N.E. India 1953–55; C.M.O., 1955–58; M.O., Dhariwal, N.E. India, 1959–64.

Dr. John Cook. Chikankata, 1957–58; Nidubrolu Hospital, Madras and Andhra (India) 1958–60; A.M.O., Chikankata, 1960–65; M.O. Howard Hospital, Rhodesia, 1967–69.

Valuable service has more recently been given for longer and shorter periods by non-officer doctors, *in some instances serving to keep open hospitals which otherwise would have had to close.* Such doctors have included:

Dr. J. Bennett Alexander (Great Britain). MacRobert Hospital, Dhariwal, N.E. India, 1965–68.

Dr. Stafford Bourke (New Zealand). The Salvation Army Hospital, Chikankata, Zambia, 1965–66.

Dr. Gordon Carter (Canada). The Salvation Army Hospital, Chikankata, Zambia, 1955–56; 1967–70.

Dr. Rupert Clarke (Great Britain). The General Hospital, Turen, Indonesia, 1958–66.

Dr. Terrance J. Daymond (Great Britain). MacRobert Hospital, Dhariwal, N.E. India, 1969–70.

Dr. Robert T. Hart (Great Britain). Catherine Booth Hospital, Nagercoil, S.E. India, 1967–68.

Dr. Varghese Kuruvilla (India). Evangeline Booth Hospital, Nidubrolu, 1967–68.

Dr. Stig. Petterssen (Sweden). Howard Hospital, Rhodesia, 1969–70.

Dr. David Senior (Great Britain). The Salvation Army Hospital, Chikankata, Zambia, 1967–68.

Dr. Bramwell Southwell (Australia). Evangeline Booth Hospital, Ahmednagar, W. India, 1964–66.

WILLIAM NOBLE

U.S.A.

WILLIAM ALEXANDER NOBLE, a Scot by birth, emigrated with his parents in childhood to the United States of America and, having qualified as a pharmacist and received his degree in medicine, served in France with U.S. troops as a medical officer in the First World War.

Earlier, as a young Salvationist, William had been greatly influenced by his mother's stories of Dr. Wille's work in Java (see Part I, Chapter 4). He had shared with her his conviction of God's call to a similar ministry. ' Where his own call would lead him was then a mystery. But he was certain of the divine origin of the call and of his own complete commitment to its demands. During a Sunday night meeting in the small Atlanta Salvation Army hall, William Noble stood on his feet, made his way down the aisle, and knelt in prayer and submission at the simple altar. There he made his lifetime dedication to God, to The Salvation Army, and to the healing of mankind.'[13]

Shortly after the First World War, he became a Salvation Army officer and, with his young wife, was sent out—immediately following their marriage—to India, their first appointment being to the Thomas Emery Hospital, Moradabad.

When, after eleven months, Noble was in the midst of presenting to his leaders plans to establish a dispensary in a nearby village, they ' commended his vision but interrupted his presentation ', to inform him that orders had been received from London for him to proceed south to assist Colonel (Dr.) Percy Turner at the Catherine Booth Hospital, Nagercoil, Travancore. He was later to succeed Colonel Turner as Chief Medical Officer at Nagercoil, an appointment he held for more than forty years, and during the course of which he was responsible for extending the facilities of the hospital immeasurably.

Dr. Turner, before him, had expanded the hospital compound to eight main buildings and opened branch hospitals in Aramboly, Chempanvilai, Kothanallur and Kulathummel. Although these were substantial accomplishments, William Noble realized there was much still to be done. More general surgery would be called for than in earlier days, and there flamed within him the hope and desire that he might ' by his own energy and enthusiasm and the

41

willing help and compassionate spirit of his loving wife and with the blessing of God ' be able to ' find new friends and benefactors to help raise the standards of equipment and personnel and expand the hospital's capacity and services '. Throughout the years he was to spend in India, the Colonel's faith and energy in outreach to new opportunities were strongly marked, and included, among other ventures, a pioneering work amongst leprosy sufferers in the State of Cochin, at the request of the state medical officer.

Establishing and developing the Cochin State Leprosy Hospital called for inordinate demands upon his time, strength and skills. As he organized, trained and supervised personnel, made periodic visits, adding to his own operating load, he did his best to cheer staff and patients and keep the hospital running smoothly. His own dedicated spirit radiated a warmth that was compelling. From the beginning he was ready to stretch himself to capacity at the call of need.

'William was constantly besieged with requests urging the extension of medical services and dispensaries in areas where there were no facilities at all. Fully conscious of the limitations of funds and staff, he nevertheless inspected every area from which he received such a request. Where the need was great, he would leave one nurse, two if possible, or a compounder, to provide a measure of first aid to the village people. Then he began to buy or beg a piece of land on which to erect a small dispensary.'[13] This readiness to alleviate suffering marked all his endeavours from the earliest decade to the latest. ' I must do all I can for anyone who is hurt or suffering,' he would say, and in every endeavour he had the full and compassionate backing of his partner.

Among the innovations for which the doctor was responsible at the Catherine Booth Hospital were the Golden Jubilee building, housing an operating theatre, erected in 1948; the first two-storey buildings, one of which he opened in 1954; a reconstruction of the hospital meeting hall, or chapel, enabling it to hold 300 people and opened in the doctor's last year; and a three-storey nurses' home. The Catherine Booth hospital compound had been enlarged from eight mud-brick buildings in 1920 to forty-six concrete, granite, and more substantial edifices in 1948, and by 1960 the number of buildings totalled sixty-four. When, in 1957, he was awarded the Order of the Founder the citation read: ' Colonel Wm. A. Noble, M.D., F.A.C.S., F.I.C.S., pioneered Salvation Army leprosy work in India, specialized in eye surgery and established branch hospitals throughout Travancore; his thirty-six years' ministry brought healing to countless multitudes; whether ministering to the prince or the poorest of his people, his Christian character has been expressed in all the ministry of heart, mind and hand.' The Colonel had earlier (1931) been the recipient of the Kaiser-i-Hind Silver Medal.

Lieut.-Commissioner (Dr.) Harry Williams has written, 'As the years went by William Noble was able to add building after building, backed by the generosity of his wide circle of friends in the U.S.A., improving the calibre of equipment and increasing bed capacity tremendously. With passing years he was able to give expression to his deep interest in those who suffered from leprosy and cancer, opening leprosaria in Northern Travancore and acquiring first radium then a deep X-ray unit for the base hospital.'[14]

With his wife, William Noble served long and competently. The couple's official retirement date was eventually set for August 25, 1961. In the meantime they strained every effort toward improving hospital buildings and strengthening staff. On December 1, 1958, the two-storey Madhavan Thampi Memorial women and children's medical building was officially opened, followed in 1959 by the laying of the foundation stone for the new hospital chapel. During the visit of Commissioner Norman Marshall, National Commander in the United States, to Southern India as the time of retirement for Colonel and Mrs. Noble drew near, the American leader paid high tribute to the outstanding service of the doctor and his wife. ' It has been my joy to know Colonel and Mrs. Noble for many years,' he said. ' I have been touched by their spirit and their wonderful faith. Nothing has been impossible with them. Knowing the great need of the people of India and knowing how much God cares for all His children, the Nobles were always sure that in some way, at some time, these needs would be met. Never asking for themselves, they could in utter simplicity and unselfishness ask largely *for their people*, and the answer always came.'

Farewells were marked by printed and spoken messages by the score, from high and low. In one village more than 2,000 villagers waited to salute Colonel Noble and his party with garlands and fireworks. Mrs. Noble found it especially trying to leave the Catherine Booth Hospital by ambulance at the beginning of the long journey home, but she was a sick woman by this time and only after she reached America did her strength begin to grow and improve.

Though both revelled in the love and closeness of family and friends, William's heart and mind were restless. ' His dedication to India had been made for life—not merely until retirement. Somehow, sometime, in some way, he must return to his adopted country.' After a period at home in Atlanta, the Colonel asked to return to India. Writing to The Salvation Army's International Leader, General Wilfred Kitching, he asked: ' Would you allow me to return for a year or two to help in the most difficult spot you have there? I fully realize that I have given my best to India. At the same time, I believe I have some reserve strength left to devote to the Lord in that great land.'

Colonel Noble was thereupon given the task of renovating and re-activating the old Emery Hospital in Anand, which had fallen on difficult days. Joined later by his devoted wife, he re-organized and re-established the hospital, where he was able to enlist the full-time services of well-qualified doctors, of whom Dr. P. K. Emmanuel, F.R.C.S. (Edin.), an Indian Methodist, served as Chief Surgeon for six years after he left.

Though he had once more to travel home because of a condition which necessitated surgery to remove his left arm and shoulder, Dr. Noble returned yet again with his wife to India in 1964, to serve further in upgrading the hospital at Anand, and ' above all to train others as carefully as possible to take over medical and administrative responsibilities '. When, in May, 1965, they returned again to America, Colonel and Mrs. Noble had completed an incomparable *forty-five years of missionary service* as active and retired officers, and Dr. Noble had been honoured by the Emory University in Atlanta, his *alma mater*, with the degree of Doctor of Humanities (1964). For Etna Noble, ' promotion to Glory '—as Salvationists refer to a comrade's passing—came in December, 1965.

The devoted couple fully epitomized William Noble's own description of the true missionary who, as he has written, ' serves with a heart full of love toward God and for the people among whom he works. He augments that love with kindness and a devotion that motivates him to exert every effort to relieve misery and alleviate suffering. . . . Missionaries are trained to give second-mile service. They set the pace for high standards. They render quality plus service '.

The story of William and Etna Noble is told in a definitive biography, *The Double Yoke*, by Lillian E. Hansen and published by The Citadel Press, New York. Colonel Noble was married to the author in 1967. An unofficial visit they both paid in 1970 to the scenes of Doctor Noble's earlier service in India was full of rejoicing and recognition by former patients and staff. Indian meals enjoyed in the homes of some of those he had helped to train in medicine, greetings in the city and by the wayside from former patients who recognized him delightedly, and inspection of the hospitals—especially the ' Catherine Booth ' where a fellow-American, Major Lyle Alloway, was carrying on the ideals of service to patients and encouragement to staff—brought deep pleasure to the ageing but still radiant servant of Christ, who had set out to India nearly half a century earlier with no desire but to serve, and who certainly has seen the reward of his labours, to the second and third generation and more, in his own lifetime.

A. BRAMWELL COOK
Chapter
Two
New Zealand

A. BRAMWELL COOK is the son of pioneer Salvation Army officers. His father, who first attended Salvation Army meetings at Regent Hall, London, and later became an officer from Battersea, travelled from Great Britain to Australia in a party led by Commissioner T. Henry Howard, an early-day Salvationist leader, in 1888. Later he served on Norfolk Island and in New Zealand.

Bramwell Cook himself was born in Gisborne, New Zealand, in 1903. Described as ' amazingly robust, always alert ', his training in physical fitness began early in life. Though a keen ' swot ' at school—Waitaki Boys High School, regarded as ' the Eton or Harrow of New Zealand ', provided full scope for that—he had even earlier proved his prowess at rugby football and taken a lively part in athletics. A keen Salvationist, he linked up with the Student Christian Movement as a youth and came to the end of a particularly successful school life with the prayer, ' Lord, I want to use any knowledge I may gain for You and for Your Kingdom. Guide me and let me know what You want me to do with my life.' He was, as yet, unaware of the vocation to Christian medicine that was to become all-compelling. All he knew was that he wanted ' to serve God and humanity '. Perhaps it would be through an arts career. The idea of teaching had a certain appeal. University opportunity was wide open to him.

It was while attending councils for Salvationist youth that young Bram Cook was challenged through a question spoken from the platform by the leader of the meetings: ' Is there any young man in this meeting, attending the university, who will dedicate his life to be a medical missionary? '

' Me? A doctor? Impossible,' were his first thoughts. ' I've no backing for such a project as a medical course.' However, the challenge could not be gainsaid, and the young man made his offer. No backing was forthcoming from The Salvation Army, though hopes of this had at first seemed tenable. Nonetheless, a Salvation Army officer, a friend of the family, became the instrument through which news of the young man's willingness to follow a medical course became known to an Australian sheep-farmer, a Christian whose own hopes of missionary service had not materialized. With his backing, Cook went ahead.

He obtained his first medical training at Otago Medical School where, after a preliminary year at Auckland, he gained the Medical Travelling Scholarship for New Zealand and, later taking his diploma in the London School of Tropical Medicine, obtained the Duncan Memorial Medal, in 1930. His degree list grew to greater length with the years: B.A., M.D. (New Zealand) F.R.C.S. (Edinburgh) M.R.C.P. (London) F.R.A.C.S., D.T.M. and H. (England).

In 1932 he received his first appointment as a Salvation Army officer (having entered training from Battersea, London) and, after some study in ophthalmology, proceeded to India, to take charge of the Emery Hospital at Anand. Arriving in Bombay, Cook was given an enthusiastic welcome to India. He was shown something of the work of The Salvation Army in Bombay. The terrible poverty of the people gripped him, but he was completely satisfied that here in this needy land was ' a glorious opportunity of serving God and man '. Cook's reaction to challenge was always positive. He was an individual marked by ' an infectious enthusiasm and complete dedication to God '. ' I feel at home already,' he told the Territorial Commander. ' I can see I have come to a people who need what I can bring. How grateful I am now for every hour of preparation I have had.'

'Anand means " happiness ".' Bramwell Cook seized upon the information with relish. The words quickly became a kind of slogan. Often he was to remind his patients, 'Anand means " happiness " ', coaxing a smile from them before he would provide medication! At the Emery Hospital, which was to be his base for more than a score of years, he found, waiting to receive him, ' Dr. E. Shmotin, a White Russian refugee woman who had fled to India after the First World War and had been in temporary charge of the hospital for a year, having served there for several years. With her were two officer nurses, Adjutants Quinn and Smith, and a number of Indians '.[15]

Before twelve months were up, Dr. Cook had increased the number of Indian nurses from two to five, and the men dressers from four to six. Dr. Shmotin was to remain for three or four years more. She retired and died in India.

The benefits of the hospital, Cook had found, ' were extended into the villages by the indigenous officers who worked in some 300 Gujerati villages. They were supplied by the hospital with medicaments and encouraged to render elementary attention. The medical officer was often asked to visit sick people in the surrounding villages, sometimes travelling forty or fifty miles to see a patient, often in the middle of the night '.[15] In the first twelve months Bramwell Cook was to make 143 such visits.

'A dispensary at Cambay City was affiliated to the hospital and another at Muktipur, a village founded and peopled by Salvationists in a time of famine some thirty years before. Bramwell discovered that both were run by officers with long experience in nursing and dispensing. Subsequently he visited these dispensaries monthly.'[15]

Cook was soon immersed in the study of Taylor's Gujerati Grammar, reading avidly about Indian customs and making his first attempts to master the Gujerati tongue. (He was eventually to become known as ' The White Gujerati '—a testimony to the completeness with which he had made himself one with the people.) He was soon learning, too, that treatments usually followed by improvement in the patient in other lands did not necessarily have the same effects in India. ' Often Bramwell Cook's constant cheerfulness masked perplexity. So many different factors and influences had to be taken into consideration in weighing up a situation. The patient was often more concerned with issues other than the purely medical one.'[15]

Dr. Cook ' decided . . . to test public interest by making an appeal for a new building. His enthusiasm won response and the sum of Rs 1,500 was raised '. Only three years after his arrival, his service at Anand was recognized by the Government of the day in the award of the Kaiser-i-Hind Silver Medal.

' We are demonstrating Christianity,' he wrote to Dorothy Money, an admired young woman friend in New Zealand. ' Perhaps this may be more effective than our preaching, valuable as

E—B.W.A.

that is.' He had met the young woman, with whom he shared his thoughts by letter, through her brother, who had been a fellow-member of the Student Christian Movement at Otago University. The Money family, members of the Baptist Church, had known something of The Salvation Army through their father, an early convert in Queensland, Australia, who had served for some years as an officer before moving to settle in Christchurch, New Zealand. An introduction to the family had led to a deepening friendship between the young people; though Bramwell's convictions had brought him into Salvation Army service, while Dorothy had been following a bent toward a teaching career. In 1932, however, she had dedicated herself to God's service as a missionary teacher, and wrote to tell Bramwell of her decision.

Some of Bram's letters had told of his work and plans at the hospital—efforts to improve the drainage system, and a new labour room to help with the maternity side of the hospital. Now, while on furlough at a Salvation Army home of rest at Panchgani, south of Poona, he wrote, in answer to Dorothy's news of her dedication to missionary service: ' Now that you feel as you have written, about missionary work, dare I ask you some day to come with me to India? I love you, Dot, and feel that in asking you this I am not only considering my feelings but am acting in accordance with God's leadings.'[15]

Although not a soldier on the Army roll, Dorothy was certainly a soldier of the Lord. She had known Bramwell Cook through her teen years. There was no one whose life she was more willing wholeheartedly to share. Salvation Army missionary service meant officership; officership presumed soldiership, and Dorothy, once her answering decision was given, followed the course which led, through somewhat unorthodox preliminaries, to officer-training in Wellington, New Zealand, and subsequent departure for India. On February 16, 1935—three years after Bramwell had arrived in India—Dorothy arrived in Bombay. Bramwell, of course, was there to meet her. They spent five days together in Bombay before travelling to Anand where, on the day after their arrival, they were married. Anand was, indeed, to mean happiness to the dedicated couple; and this—their first Salvation Army appointment as officers—was to prove a long and rewarding one. When in 1954 Bramwell Cook, having returned to his homeland, was taking up an administrative responsibility as The Salvation Army's Chief Secretary in New Zealand, he enjoyed referring to this as only his second appointment.

Among the extensions he had made to the work at Anand in

his twenty-one years—he left India in 1953—were a maternity wing, in 1937, and a tuberculosis hospital, in 1941. A training school for nurses was opened in 1943. The physiotherapy block and a deep X-ray Department were other additions that later gave him great satisfaction. He revelled in meeting the challenges of his chosen calling. ' Opportunities exist on the mission field,' he wrote, ' which would never come the way of a doctor at home. But crowning it all is the joy of leading men and women to Christ. It makes the heart of a missionary rejoice to hear a patient say, " I have never had love shown to me in my life before. If the Christian God is a God of love, I want to be a Christian." '

Of his years as a medical missionary Bramwell Cook wrote: ' I do not know any profession more satisfying and rewarding. It is the grandest in the world, for it combines in one the two noblest—the ministry of the body and the ministry of the soul.'

It is interesting to note the close study Bramwell Cook made of the subject of alcoholism following his return to his homeland. ' He had so advanced his knowledge of alcoholism that in February 1963, the *New Zealand Medical Journal* printed his article " The Aetiology of Alcoholism ", and in May of the same year he was one of the principal speakers selected for a National Seminar on Alcoholism held at Massey University College, Palmerston North.

'Although prepared to follow truth wherever it led him in the pursuit of knowledge, Colonel Bramwell Cook remained essentially simple and fundamental in his Christian faith. He believed wholeheartedly in the doctrine of conversion and saw no conflict between the belief that alcoholism was a disease and the conviction that the change brought about by the new birth could restore a drunkard.

' Colonel Cook not only took this interest in alcoholism, but he also continued his active interest in missionary work by working with CORSO, becoming a member of the national executive. This great agency for the relief of the under-privileged people in Asian and Pacific areas provided grants for many projects and Salvation Army missionary activities shared in these '.[15]

Mrs. Cook supported her husband valiantly throughout his medical missionary service, as well as in his appointment as Chief Secretary in New Zealand, and served as Territorial Home League President in the Australia Eastern Territory on his becoming Territorial Commander for The Salvation Army there. Lieut.-Commissioner and Mrs. Cook retired in 1968.

STANLEY
Chapter   # BEER
Three   *England*

STANLEY BEER, L.C.P.S. (Bombay), M.C.S.P. (London)—the qualifications might cause a measure of curiosity in the knowledgeable—was an heroic man whose Salvation Army medical missionary service in India can be said to have bridged the generations of the pioneers and their immediate successors in that land. His story is certainly an unusual one.

Gaining experience in the First World War as a serviceman with the Royal Army Medical Corps, Beer—whose boyhood had been spent in Wickford, Essex—entered training for Salvation Army officership in 1919, still wearing khaki, ' a lean, gaunt spectacled figure with a serious expression. A period of military service in India had made him aware of the vast need of the Indian people for physical healing and spiritual guidance and how few in comparison were the Salvation Army officers seeking to meet that need '.[16]

Having expressed his willingness to serve in India, Beer found himself, at the close of the training session, among a group of six officers sent to Livingstone College, Leyton, for a brief course in medical knowledge before undertaking missionary service. ' The college . . . aimed at giving prospective missionaries knowledge of first aid and medicine that would fit them to render help to their own families and those of needy people in the immediate vicinity of their work when stationed long distances from hospitals and doctors.'[16]

Later, Stanley Beer was one of a party of 100 Salvation Army officers sent to India on the s.s. *Calypso*, docking on November 11, 1921, at Bombay, where he learned that he was appointed to the Emery Hospital, Anand. The appointment proved a deferred one and he was married, while serving at Territorial Headquarters, Bombay, to Captain Annie Cherry. Even when he reached Anand at last it was to find himself in an office as cashier; however, burning the midnight oil, he applied himself to study. But ' neither his questing mind nor his compassionate spirit could be bound to books—necessary as these were '.[16]

Successively he gained access to the hospital laboratory and dispensary, before turning his attention to mastering the intricacies of the X-ray apparatus. Watching his ' chief ', Dr.

Bramwell Cook, at work in the operating theatre and being himself unqualified, though sometimes in serious demand, brought him face to face, eventually, with the need to qualify as a doctor before proceeding further in the medical service he so much wanted to be able to give.

Eventually opportunity came, after matriculating, for proceeding to Bombay to study basic medical sciences for two years and then ' walk ' the Indian medical school hospital for three years.   At the beginning of these extensive studies Beer was nearly forty years of age and had four children.   When he finally qualified to practise, he went back to Anand ' with a zeal reinforced by compassion '.   It was shortly decided to start a training school for nurses and, with Dr. Cook, Dr. Stanley Beer gladly undertook the extra work involved in preparing lecture notes.

Eyesight, long impaired, began to manifest obvious signs of weakness, however.   When, on return from his own furlough, Dr. Cook saw the seriousness of the situation he took his assistant to Bombay to consult an eye specialist.   Treatment there and, later, in 1945, in London gave partial help, but eventually the devoted doctor faced blindness, and with typical courage began to master braille.   Afterwards, three years' intensive study enabled him to add to his earlier qualifications those which gave him freedom to practise, blind though he now was, in physiotherapy. In September, 1950, with Mrs. Beer, he took ship again for India, thirty years after his first missionary voyage!   As they touched Bombay ' he and his brave wife were thrilled at the receipt of a telegram from the Emery Hospital, reading: " Welcome home." '16

A ward in the hospital was set apart for his pioneering work in physiotherapy. 'A special ward was built to house the equipment (to the value of £400) which the Royal National Institute for the Blind had given him.   Cubicles were made for individual treatment of special cases.   A new department came into being.

'As the work developed, Dr. Beer, thinking always of the future, began training students not only to assist him but to take over eventual responsibility for the extra work which he knew would be forthcoming with the extensions of the department. He began preparing students, and had the joy of piloting his first three through their studies and examinations until they too received their diplomas as physiotherapists, recognized as such by the Christian Medical Association of India.'16

When, on May 31, 1955, Lieut.-Colonel (Dr.) Stanley Beer was called to his eternal reward from Conoor, where he had gone for a period of rest with his wife, he left his beloved hospital more than a legend, or even a legacy.

At the Catherine Booth Hospital, Nagercoil, where physio-therapists are now also trained, acknowledgment is made of the fact, that so far as The Salvation Army's medical mission work in India is concerned, it was Stanley Beer who was the pioneer in this particular field.

Chapter

Four

MARGARET ROUND
England

LEAVING Tilbury, England, on New Year's Day, 1927, I looked forward to the fulfilment of my ambition (writes Dr. Margaret Round, who before that day had been keenly anticipating service as a medical missionary and who for four years thereafter was to act as Assistant Medical Officer to Dr. William Noble at the Catherine Booth Hospital, Nagercoil). I travelled from Trivandrum to Nagercoil with Mrs. Lieut.-Colonel Roy L. R. Rust, wife of an Australian missionary officer, who had just returned from taking her daughter, Gwen, to school for the first time.

My responsibility at ' C.B.H.' was that of being in charge of the women's work. I spent most mornings in a busy out-patient department, and looked after the women and children's wards, and the maternity work. A new maternity ward, with theatre, was built at this time. The district midwife lived outside the gate, and often called me to help her with village cases. I loved to walk back to the hospital as the dawn broke.

In the early part of 1931, The Salvation Army was given the oversight, and running, by the Cochin Government, of a new leprosy hospital at Adoor—now Koratty—in Cochin. I was appointed medical officer there for the first six months, until an Indian doctor obtained special training for the work—which has grown considerably over the years.

From Adoor I went to a branch hospital—about ten miles from the C.B.H. into the foothills of the tea estates. I worked there until my five-year term finished in January 1932.

I was able to do a little gynaecological surgery at C.B.H., though I felt that the only anaesthetic we had—a face mask and drop bottle of chloroform administered by an Indian nurse—was not ideal. I was very anxious to learn to do spinal anaesthetics.

Returning home, I worked in general practice in England for a couple of years and then went to Edinburgh to do post-graduate work—to try to get the F.R.C.S. exam, and learn new anaesthetic skills. The refresher courses were very helpful, but were no assistance in the matter of the anaesthetics. From Edinburgh, I went to Isfanham, Iran, with the Church Missionary Society. There, to my joy, I found that spinal anaesthetics were used for operations at twice-weekly sessions. After a year I returned to England, and again worked in general practice, and in Public Health, before I returned to India, in December 1938.

Originally I had been told I was going to women's work in the Telugu country. However, at Christmas-time in 1938, I found myself at the Evangeline Booth Hospital, Nidubrolu.

This hospital had been started by Drs. Clesson and Mary Richardson, of the U.S.A., in the mid-1930's. They did the spade work of starting a hospital in rural country, and working up some confidence in it. The nearest mission hospitals were the American Lutheran hospitals—Chirala, something over twenty miles south, and Guntur, nearly twenty miles north-west—so the work was on practically virgin soil. There were fourteen patients when I arrived—at a hospital with a general ward of twenty-eight beds, a small ward of ten beds, with baby cots, which we used for maternity and clean surgery, and two private wards.

We began to go out to the villages, seeing patients and giving health talks. We were greatly helped by the Christian Salvationist and Lutheran teachers, who advertised our coming and found a place to hold the gathering. The work began to grow. At first, before we could do any operation, or a forceps delivery of a baby, we had to get signed permission from the men folk of the family. There were a few who would not sign, and regretfully we had to let the women go home to die.

Confidence grew, and people began to request private wards; so we collected money and built five small rooms—more like cubicles—which held a bed and a locker and had a cupboard for food. The accompanying relative usually slept on the floor. These were popular rooms, at a low rent of R1 per day.

We then secured permission to build private wards. A wing was built, with a bath place and kitchen for each ward, and containing six roomy wards which, when we were very busy, were sometimes shared by two people of the same caste.

Major Ellen Evensen was my first helper and matron, and

fought the battle of cleanliness and watching for culprits stealing the linen! On her transfer, Captain Dorothy Narraway, trained S.R.N. and S.C.M., was appointed and worked some time with us. The war was on and there were staff difficulties as well as difficulty with supplies. In December 1941, at the time of Pearl Harbour, Ensign Hazel Milley came from Canada; and we were grateful for the opportunity of working together and building up the hospital work. We had to cut down most of the village visits, as we were not free to leave ' E.B.H.'. There followed a very busy and blessed time. Our Telugu officer business manager knew the people and was of immeasurable help in financing the work. He knew the wealthy people (behind the assumed rags) and we found that even a small contribution by each person gave patients more faith in the treatment. Naturally we had our few free patients, like the man who cried for the five rupee injection—he did not want the two rupee one! We found that those who could not pay the hospital bills were glad to put an ' offering ' in the box.

The war continued and my five-year term became six-and-a-half years, and I was very glad to return to England, in November, 1945. I spent the last few months, while waiting for a sailing, at the Emery Hospital, Anand, with Dr. Bramwell Cook, learning more and more about mission hospital work.

In January, 1950, I again sailed for India and Nidubrolu, to find that the little girl who had gone to school for the first time when I arrived at Nagercoil, in 1927, was now nursing sister at the Evangeline Booth Hospital, Nidubrolu—Captain Gwen Rust!

Though my own health was not at its best during this time, nevertheless, our ante-natal and maternity work grew. A Brahmin doctor at Tenali—some sixteen miles from Nidubrolu on the railway route—was an expert at eye work, and very kind to the poor, so I referred patients to him and did very little eye work during this term. I had plenty to do otherwise and had an Indian assistant—Dr. Samson from Chirala—who was a great help. She had had her own private hospital, but came to help us in Nidubrolu. Doctors from towns some miles away sent women patients for reports on gynaecological conditions and, because of our good work with the maternity patients, we began to contemplate having a training school for midwives.

A new maternity block was built in stages—first, private wards, each with their own bathing place and kitchen; then the sister's office, store room, large nursery; then preparation room and delivery room; and finally, ante-natal and post-natal wards and doctor's office for clinics. Part of these buildings were dedicated and opened by Commissioner Emma Davies, who was at that time our beloved Territorial Commander.

We hoped to have rooms built on the flat roof, for student midwives; but time flew by and those dreams did not materialize. However, we are advised to attempt great things and have faith for greater!

CLESSON AND MARY RICHARDSON

Chapter

Five

U.S.A.

CLESSON and Mary (*née* Daniels) Richardson, the American doctors mentioned by Dr. Margaret Round as pioneering the hospital at Nidubrolu, were both qualified surgeons when they offered themselves for Salvation Army medical missionary service. From New York 1, they entered training for officership in London, and were already mature in age and experience when they began their medical work with Captain rank in India in 1932 at the Catherine Booth Hospital, Nagercoil, under Dr. Wm. Noble. In 1934 they received orders to farewell and pioneer the new thirty-bed hospital at Nidubrolu and to oversight the 150-bed leprosy colony at nearby Bapatla.

Here they found themselves the only 'Europeans' in a farming community of between 20,000 and 30,000 people, who were Hindus, Muslims and Christians. The nearest fully equipped hospital was at Guntur, eighteen miles away, with a second one at Chirala, twenty-three miles away. Five acres of land for the new hospital had been donated by Pamulapati Parandayya, a local farmer, who had formerly raised bananas there.

Lieut.-Colonel Albert Senaputra, who appointed as a Captain was the hospital's first business manager (and later became Chief Secretary for the Madras and Andhra Territory), recalls that the first maternity fee paid at the hospital was a pair of country sandals! The Captain had a large share in educating patients to pay fees in money. His wife was efficient as Dr. Mrs. Richardson's interpreter and as a nurse, with R.N. status. Within six months, 'wards were overflowing on to the verandas' and hopeful patients would touch the doctors as they passed, believing that healing would come to them in so doing. As well as their internal hospital duties, the doctors also undertook wayside dispensary service with the aid of a nine-horse-power motor vehicle, so that treatment was made available to many unable to attend the hospital, while others were advised and urged to come into the hospital, where more complicated treatments could be undertaken.

When, in 1936, General Evangeline Booth visited Nidubrolu and authorized X-ray equipment, she asked if the hospital might be given her name and 'The Evangeline Booth Hospital' it became, to the delight of the American doctors, and so remains to this day. By the time the two doctors left for homeland furlough in 1938, negotiations were in hand to nearly double the acreage in order to meet expanding needs.

Early in 1940, Adjutant (Dr.) Clesson Richardson was appointed Medical Superintendent for the Yong Dong Hospital that it was planned to open in the Chung Chong Province of South Korea. Again the appointment of the doctor-and-wife-team was to a pioneering situation, though a rather different one, a new building having been raised to replace an earlier one burnt down on nearing completion after many years of planning and negotiation. But local events, in 1940, caused frustrating delays and—although staff and supplies were assembled for the hospital-to-be with much hard work—as conditions worsened politically in the Far East, the doctor and his wife, as Americans, were forced to leave the country without seeing the realization of their hopes and labours.

Following the end of the Second World War, during which the centre had been taken over and run by Japanese medical personnel, plans were made for its reopening, and Dr. Clesson and Dr. Mary returned to Korea for the purpose of reorganizing the hospital as a Salvation Army medical centre. The hospital had a capacity of seventy-five beds, serving an agricultural community of about 15,000. From the American Military Government, from Japan, from the local carpenter and other sources, the Richardsons assembled equipment for operating theatre, obstetrical department, out-patient department, laboratory and hospital kitchen. Dr. Mary devoted herself to midwifery and ante-natal work, and her husband set himself to cover other responsibilities, his first major surgery being performed in the operating theatre on October 22, 1948.

The doctor and his wife were assisted by three young Korean nurses, a Korean business manager—Captain Hor Yong—a mechanic and a hospital cook. Later a Swiss officer, Brigadier Anna Hackler, fluent in the Korean language, arrived to support

them. Later still, assistance was rendered by two English nurses—
Captain (now Major) Agnes Cage, and Senior-Captain Mildred
Stone (now Mrs. Lieut.-Colonel Philip Long). Finally came three
Korean doctors, one of whom eventually left for a three-year tour
of duty in the U.S.A.

In 1949 and 1950 conditions politically again worsened, with
raids taking place across the 38th parallel, the frontier established
after the earlier fighting, and, at the end of 1949, Dr. Clesson and
his wife had to leave for the U.S.A., for a second time disappointed in many of their hopes. They landed in New York just
two weeks before the bullets started to fly signalling the beginning
of the Korean war.

When they concluded active service in 1961, Senior-Major
(Dr.) Clesson Richardson held the position of Chaplain in the
William Booth Hospital, Covington, Ky. The couple are enjoying
the days of their retirement in a residence for retired officers at
Asbury Park, New Jersey, ' blessed for the most part with good
health and useful activities ', and testifying that, through the
years of danger and disappointment, they have had the assurance:

> Through many dangers, toils and snares,
>   I have already come;
> 'Tis grace hath brought me safe thus far,
>   And grace will lead me home.

DANIEL AND SÖLVI ANDERSEN
England and Norway

Chapter
Six

ABOUT 1919 a schoolboy walked with his father from the Salvation
Army boarding school in Fariabagh, Ahmednagar, to the railway
station about four miles away. The father, Ludwig Andersen,
wore the Indian Salvation Army uniform as to the manner born;
and no wonder, for he had been the first Norwegian Salvation
Army officer to arrive in Ceylon, in 1893, and a few years later
had been stationed in this very district of Ahmednagar, in
Maharashtra, Western India. For his first term of seven years he
had been unmarried, and wholeheartedly adopted the methods of
Booth-Tucker, India's pioneer Salvation Army missionary, walking from village to village preaching and teaching and, like the
Hindu sadhus, being dependent on the hospitality of the villagers

for food and shelter, which were rarely withheld. Now, twenty-six years later, having married and spent a period of ten years in the U.S.A., where he raised a family of three, he was back in his beloved Maharashtra.

When Daniel Andersen, the boy home from boarding school for the Christmas holiday, asked what the large stone building was on the right, about halfway on their walk, he was told it was the American Marathi Mission Hospital, run by Dr. Ruth Hume.

Who then could have imagined that, twenty years later, the same boy would return, after qualifying as a doctor, together with a medically qualified wife, to take charge of that very stone hospital, *Dagadai Davkhana*, as it was known throughout the district?

What happened in the intervening years to bring this about? During schoolboy years, Daniel had sometimes accompanied his parents to the villages. His father, with a violin which was his inseparable companion, would begin to sing and play, supported by two or three schoolboys and cadets, and soon collected a crowd; while his mother with a little ' black bag ' went to a quiet corner where she brought out her simple remedies—for the itch, for sore eyes and other common ailments—an activity to which the boy was more attracted.

At the age of fifteen Daniel accompanied his parents to Norway for a wonderful holiday, followed by schooling in England and then, at his parents' wish, a job at Headquarters. He nearly left after a few months, but was then transferred to The Salvation Army Fire Insurance Corporation—which he found congenial with a former Indian missionary, Colonel William Ward, in charge. He undertook studies in insurance and, at nineteen, qualified as an Associate of the Chartered Insurance Institute, sharing the first prize in the United Kingdom in the Fire Branch. He began to have ambitious plans for a future in insurance, but about that time was received into the home of Colonel (later General) and Mrs. George L. Carpenter, godly Salvation Army officers who became his guardians, as his parents were still abroad. The quality of their Christian character had a profound influence on the youth, who became imbued with a vision of a higher purpose than success in business and, just after Christmas in their home in 1925, underwent a life-changing experience—first, condemnation of the selfishness and self-centredness that had ruled him, and then the acceptance of Christ as Saviour and Master.

The conviction of a calling to medical missionary service grew in young Andersen's heart and mind, and led to evening studies at Birkbeck College for the pre-medical examination. After one year he passed in only two of the four subjects, and the work had to be repeated—which proved a blessing in disguise, for it led to an open scholarship for medical studies at University College Hospital, followed by qualification in 1933. This was succeeded by four absorbing years of post-graduate experience and study, mostly in surgery, and led to an attractive prospect as a surgeon in England. But the call persisted, and one day a phone call to the International Secretary for Asia and other areas at the Salvation Army Headquarters in London indicated that Dr. Andersen was ready to enter training for officership as soon as possible. January 1, 1938, found him a cadet.

A year or two before this a Norwegian girl, Sölvi Hammer, had qualified as a doctor in her native Norway and had offered for missionary service with The Salvation Army. Her parents were local officers—her father the Corps Sergeant-Major, first at Oslo Temple and later at Aalesund, to which town he moved as an *apoteker*—a chemist keeping strictly to professional work; her mother at one time Young People's Sergeant-Major at Oslo 1, and busy in the home league then and other work later. The teen-age girl, after moving to Aalesund, rebelled against the total absorption of her parents in Salvationist activities and wanted to be gay and enjoy life, like her fellow-students; but then came a personal commitment to Christ and the call to service.

As a medical student in Oslo, Sölvi Hammer was a founder member of the Evangelical Union, which today is so strong that, perhaps alone in Europe's medical schools, it recently counted more than half of the first-year students as members.

A brief courtship, and marriage in Norway, followed commissioning, before the husband-and-wife team went out together to the Ahmednagar Hospital, which had been taken over by The Salvation Army on the agreement of General Evangeline Booth during her visit to India in 1936, in faith that doctors would be found!

At the opening ceremony, in April 1939, the senior American missionary, Miss Clare Bruce, recalled the time when Major Ludwig Andersen had lived in the area with his family, laying the spiritual foundation of Salvation Army work there, and voiced a general conviction that it was God who had led in the intervening years. She promised her mission's continued co-operation in the years ahead, an undertaking which was fully honoured. Similarly, the Society for the Propagation of the Gospel mission, which had medical work in the surrounding villages, offered co-operation which grew in succeeding years, and was fostered in the monthly meeting of all missionary and senior Indian workers throughout those years.

The hospital had been completely closed for four years when the newly-arrived doctors entered on their responsibilities, and the dust was inches thick on disused furniture and rusty instruments; but soon the place was a hive of activity. The hospital was now able to build on the reputation—established over many years—of valuable medical care by doctors of the American Marathi Mission, before it had had to close in 1935 because of the economic depression in the U.S.A. and the shortage of money and staff.

An early emphasis in the new régime was on providing facilities for major surgery which, up to this time, had been practically unavailable for a population of over 1,000,000—except for those who could afford to go to Poona or Bombay, seventy-five and about 200 miles away respectively. Attendances increased rapidly as confidence grew.

Then came the war years, when Ahmednagar had over 40,000 troops in training, besides the usual population of 60,000 in the town. The military authorities requested Dr. Sölvi to visit the wives and children in three of the large camps weekly throughout the war. ' This was so much appreciated,' writes Colonel (Dr.) Daniel Andersen, ' that when we decided to build a rest house for relatives of patients (the Indian term was *dharmshalla*, or " school of religion ", as such rest houses were traditionally attached to a temple) they subscribed about half the cost. The rest was met by the local grain and sugar Rationing Committees' profits. And what a need there was for such a place! '

Many patients came by foot or bullock cart from up to fifty or more miles away, each with six or eight relatives. After being reassured (as it was usually their first visit to a western-style hospital) the majority would leave, but the mother or mother-in-law stayed, and the place they preferred at night was well out of sight under the patient's bed. To get them to go outside to sleep in the *dharmshalla* often took the sternest voice of the doctor on her night rounds. There was an occasion when Dr. Sölvi found a man sleeping on a bed in the women's general ward.

' Who are you, and where is the patient? ' came the question.

' I'm the husband and the patient is my wife, who is under the bed,' was the answer.

Red hair means something. Dr. Sölvi had red hair and the

man left in a hurry, only to complain to Dr. Daniel, ' What could be more natural and proper? '

Dr. Sölvi's devotion to her patients was entire. Through the years she raised a family of four, but continued to minister unflaggingly to the constant needs presented at the hospital.

Patients were mostly villagers and had to be treated as such. A group of about ten arrived from a village, with various complaints, none very serious, perhaps mainly out of curiosity. After they had been given their appropriate powder, ointment or potion, they went outside and sat in a circle passing their medicine from one to another with appropriate comments. Alas, after a time they lost count of where the medicines started their rounds, so a delegate re-entered the hospital to ask for further advice!

Soon the absolute necessity for well-trained nurses led to plans for a nurses' training school, and an application to the Government. This was approved, and a start was made in a basement under a private ward, with a promise to build a suitable nurses' home and training school after the war.

Wrote Dr. Daniel: 'A visiting British Surgeon-General stumbling down the dark steps commented, " This is a rum hole! "; but a more encouraging visitor was the wife of the Governor, Lord Colville, who congratulated us on our teaching programmes and at the same time was actively concerned about the accommodation. She spoke to the Governor, and soon we were invited to apply to the Government for a grant of 50 per cent of the total cost and building permits. This was agreed and, with the help of India's first woman architect, we designed what we felt was a worthy building for the purpose. Then came Independence. Would the new Indian Government honour the pledge of the British Raj? After a few months we heard that they would, provided we encouraged the enrolment of nurses from all communities and that the non-Christian would not be under obligation to attend Christian services. To this we gladly agreed and the Lady Colville Nurses' Home arose, said at that time to be the best building in Ahmednagar. The training given is recognized in Great Britain and allows the girls to take appointments and do post-graduate work in England and elsewhere.'

Tuberculosis is the commonest of all diseases—this part of India has an incidence of at least 1 per cent—which meant at least 10,000 patients with active infective lung disease in the surrounding administrative District. At the time there was not a single ward in the whole District set apart for the treatment of tuberculosis, so money was raised for this purpose after the war.

An Indian Parsee trust contributed generously, the Bombay Government assisted and the balance came from International Headquarters. The tuberculosis wards were opened by the Hon. Rajkumari Amrit Kaur, the Minister of Health for India, who came from Delhi for the occasion and said she was glad to have the opportunity of doing so. She was a Christian and had been the personal physician of Gandhi. She made a great contribution to the massive health problems in the new India and valued the contribution made by mission hospitals.

A start was made on the underlying problem of the prevention of tuberculosis by getting the co-operation of the school authorities in Ahmednagar City and tuberculin-testing all the school children, followed by B.C.G. vaccination of those susceptible.

At present there is a further extension of this prophylactic work by Captain Melvin Brieseman, M.B., B.S. (N.Z.), and Dr. Ratan Salvi, who received his first training in the hospital as a laboratory technician and was then sent for medical training to Bombay. A number of villages have been chosen for intensive follow-up of patients and contacts, together with a general village health programme.

Other special fields developed have been in radiography and physiotherapy—and the vast problems of under-nutrition in children and the care of women in pregnancy by Dr. Sölvi.

Perhaps the story of twenty-one years at Ahmednagar is epitomised by one Hindu villager, an earlier operated patient, who said to his friend whom he brought for operation, ' You must do what the doctor says, for God has sent him to help us! '

Chapter
Seven

WILLIAM McALLISTER
Scotland

WILLIAM T. B. McALLISTER, L.R.C.P., L.R.C.S. (Edin.), is a Scot, although born in Chester, England, while his parents were serving as Salvation Army officers in that city. He thinks of his heritage as ' truly in the earth ', his mother having come of farmer stock and his father having been employed in mining. His paternal grandfather was an early supporter of the Labour movement and in those days accompanied Keir Hardie, opening his political meetings in prayer. This made for the unpopularity of the McAllister family, for the new movement was not well received by either men or masters. The son, young Archibald McAllister, made his first descent into the bowels of the earth at the early age of thirteen years, but he toiled at night classes and entered the class of Humanities at Glasgow University in the year 1891. In 1896 he became a cadet at the Salvation Army Training Home in London for a ten-week session, with Evangeline Booth, daughter of the Founder of The Salvation Army, as Principal.

Dr. William McAllister's parents served faithfully as corps officers and retired, with four children still at school, in the late 1920's. Major Archibald McAllister died before he could realize, in his family, what he had worked for in his lifetime. The two daughters of the family became nurses and three sons doctors.

William had a sense of call at fifteen years. A woman missionary visitor to the corps he attended in Edinburgh spoke of the great needs of India. She described how her husband had wielded dental forceps to great purpose, with no professional qualification. This started the young man thinking: ' Should I qualify? ' He had no particular desire for the arduous studies that would be necessary, and now thinks with some reserved amusement of the youth whose day-dreams were of a steady job, possibly in a bank, with a good chance to improve his golf!

In September 1931, he entered the International Training College in London, and in May 1932, returned to Edinburgh to begin medical studies. During this period his concern for people as individuals was already marked; the occasion is recalled when he returned from selling *The War Cry* in local public houses to bring a needy old woman personally to the hospital where he was working, because she needed physical help. Little wonder that many years later, in India, he was ' the " beloved physician ", who had a way with children, winning their confidence in such a manner that the fear, the distrust, hardening their faces would give place to smiles and laughter, enabling the necessary treatment to be carried on so much the more easily and effectively '.

Travelling to India as a single officer in 1940, he served as Medical Officer for four years at the Catherine Booth Hospital, where he was to witness a period of rapid expansion as well as to be initiated into some of the traumatic experiences of first-hand contact with the challenging problems involved when a medical missionary comes to grips with sordid but compelling needs.

Later, from 1944–45, he served as Chief Medical Officer of the hospital while Colonel (Dr.) William Noble was on homeland furlough. As the work continued, the young doctor was able to

maintain the heavy medical and surgical programme undertaken
by his senior colleague and make some advances in nurses'
training and in surgical techniques particularly. During his
service as Chief Medical Officer the school for the training of
midwives was established. The first plastic surgery for reconstruction of the face, following the excision of cancerous growth, was
performed. It was at this time that he developed his skills in ophthalmic surgery, as well as his knowledge of leprosy, and learned
to identify himself with the people who came to him for help.

He was responsible for the organization of the arduous and
dangerous task of preventive work, and treatment of children,
during an epidemic which kept him on his feet day and night in
the villages and hospital for many weeks, fighting the dreaded
scourge. (Some years later he met an Indian colleague, in Edinburgh, who recognized him as the doctor who did the ' cholera
work ' in Nagercoil.)

Following this strenuous and testing first term of service,
William McAllister returned to his own teaching school to undertake a course of post-graduate study. It was during this period he
met, at The Salvation Army's International Refresher Course
held in London (1947), Adjutant Eunice Guillot, daughter of a
French Reformed Church minister. The Adjutant, who had
become an officer in France in 1933, had already held responsible
positions in youth and editorial work. They were married later
in the year.

The couple were appointed to the Army's hospital in
Chikankata, then in North Rhodesia, the doctor to serve as
Medical Superintendent. The hospital was in the embryo state
and presented a tremendous challenge.

A medical survey was carried out of the surrounding plateau
area, and later in the section of the Zambezi Valley in closest
proximity to the hospital. The endemic diseases were discovered
to be malaria, relapsing fever, bilharziasis, leprosy, trachoma, and
so on. Following this survey, the doctor established eye work,
employing the skills already developed in India under his senior
colleague, Dr. William Noble. The ravages of the disfiguring and
damaging effects of trachoma were reversed by simple plastic
surgery. And the first cataract operation was performed. Although the hospital was without electric power or X-ray equipment, steady progress was made in laying the foundations in
surgery and medicine at Chikankata. As is described elsewhere, a
revolution in the treatment of leprosy was taking place* and,

* See ' Leprosy ', p. 140.

while the doctor was Medical Superintendent there, the first patient was treated with the new drug, DADPS.

The Government of North Rhodesia approached The Salvation Army with the request for them to commence training for nurses at Chikankata. William McAllister was asked to compile, in consultation with the Chief Medical Officer for the country, the syllabus for a nursing course suitable to young African women.* Here the doctor's Indian experience stood him in good stead, as he had been involved in the setting up of the Army's first missionary Nurses' Training School in India on modern lines. Before the McAllisters left Africa for India, in May, 1951, with their two children, the first two African girls ever to be trained in nursing had passed their examinations, the first leprosy patient had commenced the new drug treatment, eye work had been begun and plans for extension at Chikankata were under way.

The India with which William McAllister was now to become acquainted was not that of his first years as a missionary: it was the North—Dhariwal, Punjab; and in 1951 the Punjab was just recovering from the terrible effects of partition. The area was still lawless, and there flowed into the hospital a constant stream of those whose injuries had been inflicted on each other by rival parties. The country was newly independent, and many difficult situations were encountered and had to be worked through. The Medical Services of the State were rapidly extending and higher standards were demanded. Before a nurse could be accepted for training she had to procure a matriculation pass; the previous standard had been much lower.

A new emphasis was made upon preventive medicine, and the teaching of this subject to the nurses. There had long been a great need for the care of eye conditions in the area, particularly trachoma. A high proportion of the population suffered from this disease and many become blind from its effects. The doctor was able to introduce the teaching of preventive medicine into the nurses' curriculum and establish eye work.

Hundreds of patients arrived at the hospital from the surrounding area. McAllister enlisted the help of distinguished eye surgeons, but for most of his years in Dhariwal he worked single-handed, operating on as many as one hundred cataracts a month. This work was not an unsupported effort, however, for Scottish Salvationists responded well to the call to ' pay and pray ' and donated well over £1,000 to this special ' extra ' in Dhariwal.

In the fourteen years spent in Dhariwal the McAllisters worked

* See p. 123.

in extensive floods in 1955, a malaria epidemic in 1956 and, not long before leaving India, they were caught up in the Pakistan–India war.

Mrs. McAllister shared the work with her husband and records the family involvement: ' My husband would often speak aloud his question marks, his hesitations, as to what was the best course of treatment. I have seen him going back again and again to see a patient he had operated upon; getting up during the night, saying: " I'll just pop over to the hospital." This, of course, gave assurance to the watching and worried relatives. To know of his concern, and to see him there, made them feel secure, content and at peace.

' In all this our children also shared. I remember so well my husband saying, one evening at our family prayers:

> " O Lord, bless, in the ward:
>   the little girl who cannot eat,
>   the little boy who cannot sleep,
>   the little girl who cannot walk."

' Such words pulled us out of ourselves, away from petty grievances or grumblings. Our children often went over to the children's ward and learned to give of their little to those who had much less.'

After twenty-six years' work overseas, much of which has been that of a pioneer, William McAllister returned to London. He had been given a new vision of its needs. The question had earlier posed itself, in the bungalow in North India where he was living: ' Who are the homeless men of London's concrete jungle? ' The question is still with him a ' hot one ' and, with a team of professional assistants, he has been engaged on another pioneer project—this time in the Men's Social Services in the United Kingdom, dealing with the problems of drug addiction, alcoholism and mental disability. He believes that ' the concrete jungles of the West present a challenge as great as, if not greater than, those of the East '. Just as, overseas, he once met the mutilated and outcast leprosy sufferer with his pressing and debilitating needs, in England he has met the ' unwanted ' of the great cities, with their often unspoken but recognizable plea for deliverance.

Asked what he sees as the possible future course for medical missionary work overseas, he says:

' The work must develop within the context of time and place for each hospital: there cannot be an over-all pattern. Still the most important function is the teaching and training of nurses and medical personnel generally, including doctors who come to us. In every place the teaching is important.

'At Dhariwal, where we established eye work, we were a hospital for the local community. In the areas surrounding the hospital there was a considerable need, particularly as so many (95 per cent of the population) suffered from trachoma. Hence the development of ophthalmology. Also, although we were a small hospital, we were able, as a result of our training programmes, to supply the needs of the training school at the much larger Christian hospital at Ludihana. Here was a case not of dependence but of a symbiosis. It is interesting to note that today (1971) we have knowledge of ten nurses, originally trained at the MacRobert Hospital, Dhariwal, working in London, some of whom will be returning to serve in India.

'At Chikankata the picture was different, because of the sparsely scattered population. Attention to the needs at hand has led to influence over a wide area, and development of the leprosy work for the province.*

' In both countries preventive medicine can be more important than specialist surgery, but the preventive programme needs to be linked to an on-going programme of specialist work—such as eyes, plastic surgery—to give any Christian hospital the status it needs in the area in which it functions. At the same time there is a place for looking at the danger of the duplication of what other Christian hospitals may be doing, and this is to be avoided where it is likely to arise.'

The work in which Colonel and Mrs. McAllister have been involved can be summed up in Mrs. McAllister's words: ' In thinking about these years there is one thing I see, I know, I feel: the presence of God. God was always there, at all times, in all circumstances.'

Chapter
Eight

HARRY WILLIAMS
England

LIEUT.-COMMISSIONER HARRY WILLIAMS, O.B.E. (1970), L.R.C.P. (Lond.), F.R.C.S. (Edinburgh), successor to Colonel (Dr.) William Noble as Chief Medical Officer at the Catherine Booth

* See ' Leprosy ', p. 140.

Hospital, Nagercoil, India, and later, from 1969 to 1970, Territorial Commander for Southern India and now for New Zealand, had two generations of Salvationist local officer tradition behind him when, as a young bandsman, a growing conviction that God would reveal His purpose for Him in his own time culminated, in 1933, in application for Salvation Army officership.

This step followed a visit to the home of Colonel (Dr.) Percy Turner, then the Army's Chief Medical Officer in England and earlier a pioneer of The Salvation Army's medical missionary work in India: in fact, founder of the Catherine Booth Hospital itself. Young Williams had told Colonel Turner that the pulpit had little attraction for him *compared with the desire to help those in physical need*, for the conviction that it was as a doctor he should serve his Master had grown steadily within him, and he had already begun his medical studies, passing the first professional examination of the Royal College of Physicians and Surgeons in 1933.

Colonel Turner suggested an interview with Commissioner Arthur Blowers (International Secretary for Asia and other areas at the Salvation Army International Headquarters) and when the Commissioner had impressed Williams that training for Salvation Army officership would be advisable before continuing his medical studies, he forthwith secured candidates' papers, promptly filled them in and, three months after the officer-training session had opened at the International Training College, Denmark Hill, became a cadet. Not for two years was he back to medical studies, at The London Hospital; but four years later he was able to take his 'finals', several months earlier than originally scheduled because of the imminence of the Second World War.

When the examinations were over, he asked for official sanction for his engagement to Lieutenant Eileen Neeve, daughter of well-known officers in the United Kingdom, whose brother had studied with him at ' The London ' and shown him the ropes. Once qualified, young Captain Williams found events moving swiftly. War was declared and the International Secretary phoned to ask if he would be ready to sail for India at short notice. Wedding at Caterham on Saturday, November 11, 1939, honeymoon on Sunday, and interview at International Headquarters on Monday, was the programme; but the passage was delayed, as ships were being redirected all over the world at that time and it was not until December, 1939, that the couple set out for India. They landed at Ceylon, crossed by ferry to India and travelled by slow train through the length of the sub-continent to Moradabad, then in the United Provinces. It was a cold, sunny day when they arrived at the Thomas Emery Hospital, and the snows of the Himalayas gleamed on the horizon.

Sixteen months later, Adjutant Edgar Stevens, F.R.C.S., with whom Captain Williams had been working as assistant, left for war service, becoming a surgical specialist with the rank of Lieut.-Colonel. Two years afterwards the hospital was taken over (with The Salvation Army's consent, as in the First World War) as a military base hospital, and Harry Williams became a Captain in the Indian Medical Service and was transferred first to Lucknow and then to Poona for grading as a surgeon. During the time in Poona their first child, three-year-old Ann, died; a sudden inexplicable blow for Harry and Eileen Williams.

When International Headquarters cabled a request for Dr. Williams's release, its receipt was followed by an order, from the India Office, placing him on 'the employed list, for service of civil importance'. This proved to be at the MacRobert Hospital, Dhariwal, in the Punjab. The eighteen months of military service, though unsought, had proved excellent experience in the field of orthopaedics. Homeland furlough, after seven years' absence, was taken in the United Kingdom; Harry studied at Edinburgh and was elected F.R.C.S.

At the end of his second term in India, a year at the Catherine Booth Hospital, Nagercoil (with Dr. Noble as C.M.O.) gave Harry Williams evidence of problems in orthopaedic and cancer surgery, especially of the mouth, where the condition is due, it is thought, to betel-nut chewing, a widespread habit among the villagers.

With the momentous changes taking place in independent India, the medical missionary outlook was altering—some hospitals were closing and others 'losing out' in comparison with the improving Government standard. Williams felt that a measure of specialization was the best way to counter this trend, and his next furlough in the United Kingdom found him at the East Grinstead plastic surgical centre, working under Sir Archibald McIndoe. Before he left he was proposed for Associate Membership of the British Association of Plastic Surgeons, and elected. (Election to full membership came in 1960.)

Meanwhile, when Dr. Bramwell Cook said good-bye to India, Harry Williams had the task of following him to the Emery Hospital, Anand, which had come to be affectionately known, during his predecessor's twenty-one years of service in the area, as 'Cook's Hospital'. Williams had the distinction of being the first plastic surgeon in Gujerat, and proved the value of specialization when patients began to come from long distances for this treatment. Here he carried out the first experimental operations for leprosy deformities and was grateful to Major Ken Tutton, M.S.R., who took the photographs, in the operating theatre or studio, for subsequent documentation. Twenty scientific papers, over as many years, were published in the medical journals in the United Kingdom, India and the U.S.A., and more than this number of papers read at conferences and in medical colleges.

When, on the retirement from active service of Colonel (Dr.) Wm. Noble, Harry Williams was appointed Chief Medical Officer at Nagercoil, his previous experience stood him in good stead, and the reconstructive surgery he practised at the Catherine Booth Hospital soon developed branches; first a Physiotherapy Department, then rehabilitation and, finally, a separate institution for vocational training for the physically handicapped. Homeland furloughs also were made to bear fruit in The Salvation Army's total healing ministry. On leave, during the nine years spent at Nagercoil, Harry Williams learned from Sir Herbert Seddon new techniques in orthopaedics.

What an amount of paper, too, has been covered with drawings for new or remodelled buildings! And how providential that Harry Williams's early training in insurance underwriting should have included plan-drawing, building design and construction, since each hospital in which he has served—and he has served in more than any other Salvation Army officer-doctor in India—has seen a new ward, theatre or special department.

Known to his Salvationist comrades at home as a gifted artist and above-average writer on various subjects for 'Army' periodicals, he is an attractive speaker (his distaste for public speaking has long been well overcome through the needs of the salvation war and rigorous self-discipline), he is appreciated by colleagues of the medical world as a specialist in his own field. Called on to aid relief work in Vietnam, he spent three months as senior surgeon, setting up the first plastic surgical unit in that country, where his medical staff knew him not as Colonel, but as Professor!

How does Lieut.-Commissioner Harry Williams see Christian medical work in today's context?

A postscript to his book *Miracle of Medicine Hill* (1970) gives the answer:

' We live in an age in which the attitude to those who engage in humanitarian work is " give him the tools, brother ", but if such work is part of a church programme and the worker avowedly evangelical, the public's ardour cools. To help church-orientated social work is equated with sharing the church's beliefs and the church's constituency has shrunk. We have our modern Thomas Huxleys, who regard good works as cheap propaganda, subverting the mind. Many Hindus are suspicious of missionary schools and hospitals as part of the programme producing so called " rice Christians ".

' Christ constantly refused to give the " sign ", the magical proof of His divine appointment, but pointed seekers to His day-by-day ministry as the proof of His Messiahship. Neither did He indulge in huge impersonal schemes to root out all evil or disease. Even His temptations have a bearing here. What He did do was to show at every turn God's love and concern for the individual. He healed not by public health measures, but by personal, individual confrontation. Peter and John, His disciples, continued in like manner. " In the name of Jesus Christ of Nazareth, rise up and walk," they said to the cripple at the temple gate. Of course, good government, sound public health departments, propaganda and education can well be Christian callings, but the Church is called in every generation to reveal Christ. This is an art which involves hand and heart as well as brain. It is not primarily a matter of dogma, preaching or education, but a living witness of the full-blooded type which Christ Himself gave. God *is*, He *cares*, He is *involved*, is Christ's message continuing in His Church. It must show personal concern and evoke love and faith.

' No better avenue is open to Christians than medical work of the type described in this book. That is my simple credo. We could do with such institutions in the West, for the care of the sick is a subject for which science alone is inadequate. Medical science claims all the success, but who will know what a nurse's human kindness and faith have meant in any individual's restoration to health? As to the future—well, if my credo is accepted, the need for such hospitals continues. But it can hardly be in accord with such a belief to perpetuate hospitals whose professional standards have not kept pace with the contemporary scene. And it must be admitted that medical care has shown an ever-increasing appetite for men and money. Perhaps the Church cannot afford it, the price, that is, in terms of pounds or dollars. More likely the Church cannot afford it in terms of dedicated personnel. The price the young doctor pays in embarking on a missionary career is greater than ever. He quickly reaches the point of no return as far as a professional career in his homeland is concerned. The gulf between income and comfort is still as wide as in Victorian days. He may have a refrigerator today, but the television, the social round, the congenial worship and culture are lost, and in an alien milieu he works long hours with a tithe of the support in staff and equipment which he knew as a house surgeon.

'But to be a fisher of men is still greater than being a simple fisherman. And Christ still calls men from perfectly good and healthy pursuits to ones more difficult, involving discipleship with its hardships, but with His sustaining grace.'

Chapter

Nine

SIDNEY GAUNTLETT
England

SIDNEY GAUNTLETT, M.B.E. (1959), M.B., B.S. (Lon.), D.T.M. & H. (England), was born into a Salvationist home with the highest traditions of service to others. 'I had seen something of the sacrificial service given by my parents in God's work,' he says, 'although . . . I had only a little idea of what it had really cost them. When I was a young boy of thirteen attending at grammar school and having been afflicted with a good deal of ill health, the idea that one day I should be a medical missionary was probably . . . a combination of natural ambition, a sense of adventure and an understanding sympathy for the sick.'

Though at one time it seemed uncertain whether health would allow him to work overseas as a medical missionary, with the years conviction grew in young Gauntlett that his calling was to serve God as a Salvation Army officer and doctor. 'As the years passed, the spiritual implications of this conviction became clearer,' he has written, 'and I was willing to trust Him to the limit. . . . When I qualified in medicine my main reaction was a great gratitude to God for His help and guidance and, still with a sense of unworthiness, I offered my life again to Him for service.'

Sidney Gauntlett entered training for Salvation Army officership from Wood Green. In 1947 he was commissioned as an officer and married in the following year to Lieutenant Violet Markham, a Salvationist from the same corps; then he proceeded to his first overseas appointment—The Salvation Army's Mac-Robert Hospital, Dhariwal, in the Gurdaspur District of the Punjab.

Writing of this experience and his subsequent introduction to medical work in Zambia (or Northern Rhodesia as it was when he was transferred there in the early 1950's), he commented: ' Soon I realized how little I had given.'

'Amidst the appalling poverty and filth of an India in its early struggle as an independent nation and later in disease-stricken Africa, where people were just beginning to emerge from pagan darkness, my equipment seemed all too inadequate, and any thought of sacrifice faded for good. I had never conceived that there could be such suffering in the world.'

' Christ called His disciples to teach, to preach and to heal,' Sidney Gauntlett has written, ' and to medical missionaries is given the privilege of being actively engaged in all three. . . . The rich rewards and privileges that have come to me as an officer are far greater than anything I gave up.'

The years have brought to Brigadier (Dr.) Gauntlett a wealth of experience and ability to cope with need. The establishment of a well-equipped settlement to house leprosy sufferers is an addition to the Chikankata hospital, where he served until 1967, that will continue to be linked with his name.

Among the emergencies of mission field service that he has good reason to recall was the occasion when, during Congress meetings conducted by General Wilfred Kitching in Rhodesia in 1958, an outbreak of smallpox was discovered and he, with a team of Salvationist nurses, vaccinated more than 15,000 people on the Congress site.

The year 1970 saw Brigadier Gauntlett off to Nigeria, from the International Training College, London, where, since 1967, he had been serving as Medical Officer. In Nigeria he was to give the benefit of his experience—by request of the National Rehabilitation Department of the Nigerian Government—to on-the-spot discussions concerning proposals under consideration for mentally retarded or war-disabled children, as well as permanently disabled ex-servicemen.

Brigadier Gauntlett has reckoned one of the most rewarding services he has been able to render to his fellows while absent from the scene of most of his life's labours has been a ministry to young people sometimes described as ' drifters ' on the outskirts of society in London.

Asked for his observations on Salvation Army medical work

as he sees its development in Africa, he points out the pioneer
nature of much of our medical service in that continent, over
against work in India, where medical services were already in
operation in some of the areas where our pioneering was done.
' Because of the need and the lack of medical coverage, our
emphasis has been on curative medicine, gradually gaining the
confidence of the people, and overcoming their suspicions of the
white man,' he says.   ' In time there has come an increasing
emphasis on preventive medicine, which includes child care,
health education, preventive inoculations, and so on.   The
problem is to achieve a balance of the curative and the preventive.
The latter inevitably demands a long-term view of the effectiveness of our work, the establishment of better sanitation, water
supply, housing and general cleanliness, which forms a much
better investment than the provision of medicines for the sick.
*From the point of view of long-term planning, we must think less of
buildings and more in terms of mobility in out-reach.*

' In most parts of Africa, Christian medical work is in rural
areas, which are often neglected—Government personnel prefer-
ring to work in urban areas, where the Government is prepared
to provide specialist services. This situation, together with the
fact that very few doctors are available, means that we have to
spread ourselves over the whole range of medicine, that is, be
general practitioners rather than consultants. We have to be
adaptable, changing our policy according to local needs and
provisions, and this applies to emphases on T.B., leprosy treatment, training programme and preventive work. Failure to adapt
will render our work superfluous.

' It must also be remembered that with the increasing emphasis on the participation of nationals, and restriction of entry
for expatriates, we must step up our training programme to
ensure that, when the time comes and expatriates are completely
excluded, there will be the necessary number of national personnel
to take over.

'A factor to be recognized by western-trained personnel coming newly into the African scene today is that they will find, in
the course of time, that the national nurses, the range of whose
training is less wide than that of the S.R.N. personnel of the west,
are nonetheless trained to taking a greater medical responsibility
in their own areas than the more highly trained missionary nurse
has herself undertaken at home.

' Finance to some extent dictates policy, as where no Government subsidy is available, there is a tendency to concentrate on

private practice and surgery, which bring the necessary income to support the hospital. We must take care to avoid this, and so encourage (a) the national Christians to give more in support of the medical work in their own land, and (b) the patients to pay for the service given, as their own standard of living increases. Most of those who know the situation would agree that for a long time yet we must be prepared to subsidize our medical work from overseas.

' Population control is important. Unless we are aware of the very serious trends, our well-meaning efforts to save life and eradicate disease may bring about disaster, unless balanced by a vigorous agricultural programme and wide and carefully organized planning. The whole question of the treatment of the individual, *vis à vis* the community as a whole, arises; and we are faced with the necessity to think increasingly in terms of the community.

' In Nigeria and Ghana there is a large number of doctors, whereas in Zambia and other African countries the training programme for doctors and registered nurses is in its initial stages. It will be another five years (from 1970) before the first Zambian-trained doctor graduates and the slow trickle of supply begins.

' We cannot fail to recognize the importance of co-operation with (a) Government and local authorities (b) with other Christian groups. The ideal co-operation would be that the Christian Church and the Government plan the Health Service together, to some extent pooling resources and personnel. In some countries there is a National Christian Medical Association which keeps in very close touch with the Government Ministry of Health. In Zambia an advisory committee is in operation, having missionary and Government representatives and advising the Minister of Health on planning and policy. This avoids a duplication and competition which can prove very costly.'

SARA DANIEL

Chapter

Ten   *India*

A DAUGHTER of India, Lieut.-Colonel Sara Daniel, L.M.P., who was promoted to Glory from retirement in Nagercoil on January 21, 1969, was born into a Salvationist family and, with her parents, knew from her childhood something of the self-sacrifice entailed in the task of bringing salvation to the Indian villages.

Her father was a divisional commander in South India when, in 1925, she watched a large crowd of suffering people awaiting the return from furlough of Dr. William Noble, and his wife and family, in order that they might gain some attention to their needs. The doctor and an officer nurse, who had accompanied the family, were immediately plunged into two hectic days of activity as they attended, almost ceaselessly, to the needs of the anxious people gathered at the divisional headquarters compound. An unforgettable sight was that of the crowds who remained afterwards to sit out of doors in the moonlight as the missionaries read to them from the Bible. ' Why do these people do it ? ' Sara asked herself. ' They have to work so hard; how can they go on doing it ? '

Shortly afterwards, Sara found that personal commitment to Christ's cause meant full-time Salvation Army service for her and, setting aside a teaching career upon which she had already embarked, she became an officer from Trivandrum in 1927. It was while she was serving as a Captain at the Southern India Territorial Headquarters that Sara Daniel was selected, on the recommendation of Dr. Noble, for medical training under the renowned Dr. Ida Scudder at The Christian Medical College, Vellore, Madras. When, in 1937, she returned from Vellore to Nagercoil and was appointed to the Catherine Booth Hospital as a Licensed Medical Practitioner, with special responsibility for women and child patients, this dedicated woman had found a field in which she was to serve with compassion and efficiency for more than a generation. The Women's and Children's Department made remarkable progress under her direction and the Keast Obstetric Block, opened at the hospital in 1962, was her particular joy. Nurse training also formed an important part of her responsibility.

After acquiring further experience at The Salvation Army Mothers' Hospital in London, Sara Daniel served until her retirement in 1964—and even afterwards—as the Catherine Booth Hospital's Assistant Medical Officer, giving valuable service long after she might have been justified in taking life more easily, and indeed until the arrival of Captain (Dr.) Hazel Mason. Sara Daniel had inevitably become imbued with the same loving and dedicated spirit of service as her predecessors. She will always hold a special place for the women who come after her for the shining example she set them as their forerunner.

Lieut.-Colonel (Dr.) Sara Daniel's promotion to Glory in 1969 was from the Catherine Booth Hospital, after unavailing blood transfusions, for which several of her comrades had been ready donors. It was recorded that 'those who nursed her in the last days were happy to serve one who for thirty years had cared for women in this hospital'. Dr. Varghese Kuruvilla, a surgical registrar at the hospital and a nephew of the doctor, declared: 'She never complained or fought for rights or privileges, setting a spiritual example that has influenced all who worked with her.'

Chapter
Eleven

K. C. JOSEPH
India

ANOTHER young Indian officer selected for medical training was Captain Kaipatta Chacko Joseph, who, in 1937, was awarded the L.C.P. & S. diploma from the Miraj Mission Medical School, India. The young man had been dedicated to God and officership at his birth and, having matriculated, entered training from Naranganam, Thiruvalla, and was commissioned as an officer in 1930. Following his medical training, he was appointed to the Catherine Booth Hospital, Nagercoil, and served in succeeding years at its branch hospitals at Kangazha, Chempanvilai, Radhapuram and Aramboly.

In 1939 Captain K. C. Joseph was married to Lieutenant Anna John, the daughter of a doctor in Kangazha, the ceremony being performed by Dr. William Noble. In the same year Captain Joseph was appointed as Assistant Medical Officer at the Koratty Leprosy Hospital, where he received a foretaste of what was to become a life-service of future usefulness. In the following year he was transferred to the Evangeline Booth Leprosy Hospital at Puthencruz, Kerala State, South India, where his real leprosy work began. Both these centres had been established under Dr. Noble, the latter—built to accommodate 200 patients—being officially opened by General Evangeline Booth when she visited India during 1936. 'Planned and developed as finances allowed, were separate sections for men and women, with provision for leprous and non-leprous children. . . . There were kitchens, a laboratory, library, schoolrooms and therapy rooms.'[13]

This was Dr. Joseph's field as a Medical Officer. Then, having served in the Leprosy and General Hospital at Puthencruz for nine years, he was appointed to a branch (general) hospital for six years at Kangazha and in this period, by his own efforts, built an in-patients' ward with twelve beds at a cost of 8,000 rupees.

He returned to Puthencruz as the Medical Superintendent in 1955, an office he still (in 1971) holds with distinction. Four years later he was selected as a member of a session for Salvation Army senior executive officers at the International College for Officers, in London, following which he attended a course of studies with the British Institute of Dermatology at St. John's Hospital for Diseases of the Skin, in London. He is a recognized leprologist and a member of the International Leprosy Association.

Among the developments now under Lieut.-Colonel Joseph's direction at Puthencruz are the Etna Noble Memorial Buildings, a laboratory and a workshop where patients are taught carpentry, weaving, tailoring and shoe-making in multiple rehabilitation programmes.

Mrs. Lieut.-Colonel Joseph assisted her husband in mid-wifery and dispensing during his period in the branch hospitals, and worked as diet officer for four years and dispenser for three years in the leprosy hospital, and for a number of years has had charge of the general stores of the Puthencruz hospital and carried matron's responsibilities.

Chapter
Twelve

CLIFFORD SEAMANS
U.S.A.

GOD leads in mysterious ways (writes Lieut.-Colonel Clifford Seamans, M.D., of the U.S.A., about his work as a doctor in The Salvation Army). The divine call into The Salvation Army was very definite, and equally unexpected. In 1937, at the time of the call, I was a new staff physician in a North Carolina Mountain Hospital of the Presbyterian Church. (I had been married in 1935.) We applied for Africa, were accepted for India, commissioned in February 1939, and, ten days before sailing, were appointed to China!

In Peking we were welcomed, in April 1939, to a year of language study. Before long, the need in the Salvation Army camps in the city gave me opportunity to see and treat many sick refugees who gathered from the five camps to our two camp clinics for treatment.

Harry
Andrews

Catherine Booth
Hospital, Nagercoil,
India

Weaving for leprosy
patients, Nagercoil

Percy
Turner

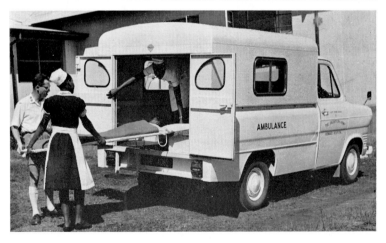

Public health teaching in a village school, India

Having fun at ' Joytown ', Kenya

Arriving at Howard Hospital, Rhodesia

Hopes of reopening the Ting Hsien hospital,* which had had to be closed, receded as the anticipated time for its reopening neared, and a call from Major George Walker to come and start a clinic in T'ient'sin, where he was Regional Officer, was discussed with Colonel Arthur Ludbrook, Chief Secretary for North China, and the decision to open a clinic in the Nan K'ai district of the region was made.

By the time Medical Military Permits were withdrawn; 60,000 visits had been made to the clinic by patients but withdrawal of permits did not mean the end of the work. Mr. Ch'i, an officer's son, had been trained, and with help from Doctor Ting and others the clinic was maintained and was still open some years later, according to rumour coming out of that country.

Many eye operations, skin tumours and ' anything that permitted transportation of the patient back home ' were done. Perhaps the most noteworthy case that remains in time-blurred memory was that of a woman member of our T'ient'sin Central Corps who had been blinded by trachoma. After protracted treatment, three operations on one eye and two on the other, she gave this testimony in a Sunday morning holiness meeting: ' For many years I have been carrying my Bible but could not read it. This morning, I can see to read.'

The need of medical work in the area might best be described in the words of our Chinese nurse, Miss T'ien, who often said, ' If *you* don't do it, no one will.'

*   *   *

After release from concentration camp at Weihsien during the Second World War, and repatriation in December 1943—via Goa, India, Port Elizabeth, South Africa, and Rio de Janiero, Brazil—we were assigned, in February 1944, to our Salvation Army general hospital in Covington, Kentucky, where we worked for the remaining war years and until September 1948. By then it was evident that further work in China was not feasible, and we were assigned to Japan.

The work in Japan was considered as post-war rehabilitation and reconstruction of the medical programme. Dr. Rin Iwasa† was carrying on under very difficult circumstances and, though it was not known at first, was in rapidly failing health. We were assigned to Sei Shin (Clean Heart) Tuberculosis Sanatorium in Kiyose Mura, and later to both Sei Shin and the William Booth

* See the Arthur Swain story, p. 33.

† See p. 30.

Sanatorium in Suginami-Ku, Tokyo, with a combined bed capacity of 435.

It was thrilling to be able to add laboratories, clinics, and a surgical unit to Sei Shin Sanatorium, as well as new heating plant and dish sterilizing equipment, and to effect much necessary renewal. At the William Booth Sanatorium, Dr. Iwasa had added a new clinic and surgical facilities, and I was able to add new X-ray and clinic facilities, and a complete and beautiful nurses' home, as well as securing much needed building renewal. This in no way detracted from our religious programmes, personal medical work, and efforts to encourage and unify the staff at both sanatoria.

The battle against disease is not always won. One evening after returning from Suginami to Kiyose, where we lived, an urgent plea was received to get a young mother with terminal tuberculosis from a neighbouring village. Out came the station wagon seats, and in went a mattress and thick comforts. One of the women doctors, my interpreter and I set out over the dirt roads to the patient's village. The grandmother seemed to have only one idea in mind, ' Get the patient out as I cannot feed and care for her—her husband has left her.' After some months of up-and-down response to therapy, the end came to the young mother. Patients and staff alike were saddened by her death, as she had waged such a cheerful, valiant battle against her disease.

Near the end of our five-year stay in Japan, Dr. Nagasaki* became Lieutenant (Dr.) Nagasaki and began his work at Suginami. Other doctors were rapidly becoming available for the medical work there.

*   *   *

Medical missions present a big question mark for the future, but my experiences lead me to believe that, where possible, medical missionaries are well advised to leave administration to nationals and concentrate on the best possible medical care and personal Christian witness to those, the suffering and poor, who need them most. This may not lend itself to prestige and fame, but gives hope, courage and comfort where it is most needed.

I saw this kind of need again and again as a member of a Salvation Army disaster team sent to Peru, in the area of the recent (1970) earthquake and mud avalanche. Captain (Nurse) Mrs. Erich Hamm and I, and later Nurses Porter and Turner, of the Anglican Church, Santiago, saw many patients from ' back in the mountains ' who had never been seen by a doctor or graduate

* See p. 81.

nurse before. Without Government or mission support doctors cannot survive in these rural areas.

What an opportunity for medical care and Christian witness awaits, where Governments permit entry to missionary teams! This is not to imply that, where needed and permitted, Salvation Army hospitals should not be continued or founded, but that, with increasing medical care available in the cities, we may be neglecting a great and needy field in rural, isolated areas which may remain open to us long after the prestigious city locations are closed to all but national hospitals. One child, brought to us as we camped by the roadside waiting for transportation back to Lima, was in critical condition and had been carried by her mother and father for four hours over mountain trails when they heard that a doctor and nurse were available at that place.

*   *   *

Following our return from Japan, we spent five years in our Salvation Army home and hospital in St. Louis, Missouri, and then were transferred to our present appointment, where we minister to the medical needs of homeless and alcoholic men in eight of the Men's Social Service centre clinics in the New York Metropolitan area. Again, a work needed by the needy—difficult but satisfying.

TARO NAGASAKI

Chapter

Thirteen   *Japan*

MAJOR TARO NAGASAKI, M.D., F.A.C.C.P. (Fellow of the American College of Chest Physicians), first met The Salvation Army during his school life. He had been growing up in a Christian home but had neglected to accept Jesus Christ as his personal Saviour. Through the active ministry of The Salvation Army he was influenced to surrender himself to Christ in his medical school days and, in 1949, was enrolled as a soldier.

After graduation from Kyushu University Medical School, in 1951, he became an intern of St. Luke International Hospital in Tokyo, a famous mission hospital, where he was tested in a decision he had to make as to whether he should enter the Army's officer training college first or spend a number of years in qualifying as a doctor before doing so. Committing himself to God in prayer, he was guided to enter the training college in 1952 and was commissioned to the Booth Memorial Tuberculosis Sanatorium, Suginami-Ku, in 1953. He was then permitted by Territorial Headquarters to spend three years at the St. Luke International Hospital in order to qualify in internal medicine.

Following qualification, he spent three years gaining a Ph.D. from Tokyo Medical College for his study of industrial hygiene. Throughout these years he made every effort to give good medical service to the tuberculosis patients, following the good work put in by Lieut.-Colonel (Dr.) Clifford Seamans, M.D., of the U.S.A.

In 1956, as a Captain, Nagasaki was married to Lieutenant Hiroko Nagasawa, and they now have two sons. Mrs. Nagasaki works voluntarily at the hospital, helping the patients in occupational therapy, teaching them pottery-making and wood carving.

In 1964 Taro Nagasaki was sent by The Salvation Army to the U.S.A., where he attended an intensive six-month course on hospital administration in Columbia University, and studied chest and chronic diseases in New York Medical College for a further six months. In 1966 he was awarded the F.A.C.C.P. by the American College of Chest Physicians at their International Assembly in Copenhagen.

After being appointed as Superintendent of the Suginami Booth Memorial Sanatorium he was made responsible for plans initiated by Lieut.-Colonel (Dr.) Clifford Seamans and involving the total reorganization and replacement of the fifty-three-year-old wooden erection at Suginami, and other renewal programmes. When General Frederick Coutts visited the Sanatorium at Suginami early in 1968, the International Leader broke the ground for a new three-storied reinforced building.* On November 23 of the same year H.I.H. Princess Chichibu formally opened the building, renamed the Booth Memorial Hospital, with accommodation for 104 patients, in the presence of Lieut.-Commissioner William Parkins, then Territorial Commander of the U.S.A. Western Territory.

Major Nagasaki expresses himself as deeply grateful for divine guidance in all his planning, and for the leadership at International and Territorial Headquarters which made possible the continuation of the healing ministry in this fresh setting and the winning of suffering souls to Christ, the Saviour.†

In addition to his official Salvation Army work, Major Nagasaki has been aiding International Co-operation in Christian

* See Tuberculosis, p. 138.

† See Tuberculosis, p. 138-140.

Medical Work in South-East Asia, as part-time Secretary of the Committee of Medical Work, E.A.C.C. since 1968. In this capacity he travelled to Laos and Vietnam on a fact-finding mission in 1969, and in 1970 was nominated a member of the Advisory Committee of the Japan Hospital Association.

LYLE ALLOWAY
U.S.A.

Chapter
Fourteen

LYLE ALLOWAY (now a Major, B.A., M.D. (Chicago), Chief Medical Officer of the Catherine Booth Hospital, Nagercoil) and Ruth Nichols were attending Northwest College in Nampa, Idaho, U.S.A., and were already dedicated in their hearts to serving God as medical missionaries, when they first encountered The Salvation Army. Lyle, a pre-medical student working toward a B.A. in chemistry, and Ruth, a student nurse working for a B.Sc., were attracted to attend a youth rally to be led by ' an Englishman, named Gilliard, a Salvation Army officer from San Francisco '. Says Ruth: ' We went along. It was our first contact with the Army and we took to it like ducks to water. We began to have a conviction that God was leading us.'

Learning of The Salvation Army's medical mission work, and in particular that its oldest and largest hospital in South India was directed by an American, Colonel (Dr.) Wm. Noble, it was natural that their interest in the Catherine Booth Hospital, Nagercoil, was readily aroused.

Following the Alloways' marriage in 1949 and graduation in 1952, came four difficult years while Lyle attended Medical School in Chicago and Ruth, equipped as a B.Sc., worked as a nurse to help support them both, while they meantime continued as active Salvationists. In 1957, a year after receiving his M.D. degree, Dr. Alloway, with his wife, entered the U.S.A. Western Territory's School for Officers' Training and, when their appointment to the Catherine Booth Hospital was made, ' hope became a reality ' and they set off with joy for their long-anticipated medical missionary task. Warmly greeted by Dr. William Noble, and conducted by him ' around the maze of wards, showing us the variety of diseases presented for treatment ', the newcomers felt a certain inadequacy, and could (as Dr. Alloway was to write later)

' almost have wished ourselves safely back home, where there is an abundance of specialized skill for ready consultation '.

However, the new missionary couple were not long in becoming ' thoroughly orientated among the hospital's sixty-odd buildings ' and were soon making their own valuable contribution to its work.   The field in which Lyle Alloway's talents were particularly to find outlet was that of ophthalmology, long a speciality at ' C.B.H.', where Dr. Percy Turner had set a precedent which Dr. Noble had been proud to follow and extend.   Later, Lyle Alloway himself was to return to the University of Chicago for post-graduate work in eye diseases, and his undoubted skill was further enhanced by study and practice.

' One in five of the blind on earth are in India.   Cataract is a particular scourge,' Mrs. Alloway has said, ' and Lyle operated on its victims almost every day.   It is a terribly delicate and intricate operation and as I watch him, proud and marvelling at the sensitivity of his fingers, I can hardly believe this is the man who, as a shy teenager, acted the part of the bridegroom at the mock wedding ' (a reference to their first encounter, when in a not-too-serious sketch at the Methodist Church, Burwell, Nebraska, Lyle Alloway and she had played the parts of groom and bride in a dramatization to mark the pastor's wedding anniversary).

Writing of the work at ' C.B.H.', Dr. Alloway has said: 'A wide variety of patients are attracted to the hospital.   Numbered among them are Hindus, Mohammedans and Christians.   Rich and poor alike find an open door.   No one is refused admission because of inability to pay.   As a mission hospital, our first responsibility is to those who are unable to obtain treatment elsewhere.   This means that a large number of our patients pay nothing, or only a small portion of the cost of their treatment. Since our financial resources are not unlimited, our effectiveness depends upon the generous giving of others who are more fortunately placed. . . . Although we do not see large numbers of new Christians, the occasional convert and the words of appreciation voiced, and written, by patients . . . are a great source of encouragement.'

Let Mrs. Alloway have the last word: ' You " throw your life away " and God gives a richer, fuller life in its place.   When I see those who came blind walk out of this place, *sans* bandages, *sans* sticks, because my man has been able to save their sight, I am as happy as any rich film star, happier probably. . . . " Follow Me," Jesus said by the lakeside.   He did not offer comfort or riches, but He does give happiness.'

PART THREE

Vital Co-operation

Chapter
One

THE VALIANT NURSES

WHERE can one begin—or end—the story of the valiant nurses who have so competently and selflessly backed up The Salvation Army's missionary doctors? One solves the first problem by 'beginning at the beginning', and paying tribute to the wife of Harry Andrews who bravely aligned herself alongside her husband to help in his devoted work for the poor and suffering around them in India. Earlier, while serving as a young officer with her sister in Poona, she had bravely given practical assistance to British troops in health safety measures when the city was plague-stricken. Wearing special clothing, she had helped the soldiers to carry out the sick and dying from their homes, afterwards heaping refuse from the sufferers' rooms into great piles and setting it ablaze. She had then shown the householders how to limewash their walls and disinfect their floors.

Quite untrained in nursing skills at first, Mrs. Andrews, after her marriage, learned from her husband how to bathe and dress a wound, and how to assist him at the scene of many an emergency operation, as well as in routine procedures, though it was only during the leave when Andrews qualified as a doctor, in 1910, that his wife received any specific training herself.

Mrs. Colonel Percy Turner was the first registered nurse to function in such capacity at the Catherine Booth Hospital, South India, which her husband founded. She had trained at Maidstone, England, where she had been a nursing sister, and had proved her capacity in Salvation Army women's social services at The Nest— a children's home in London—and at Ivy House, 'the first Salvation Army hospital', opened in Hackney for maternity work, and the training of mid-wives, and the precursor of the Salvation Army Mothers' Hospital at Clapton.

She travelled to India to become the wife of the 'Catherine Booth's' first qualified medical officer, determined to give of her best to the cause her partner had so whole-heartedly made his own. From the first she assisted her husband in the hospital work with vigour, and it is recorded that 'the birth of two sons and a daughter did not cool her ardour'.[13] The pattern of training Indian personnel in nursing was soon established, and the hospital became 'a school of nursing issuing its own certificates and conducting its own examinations'.

A somewhat startling pen-picture of this redoubtable pioneer appears in a description of Dr. and Mrs. Wm. Noble's welcome to the Catherine Booth Hospital in 1921, at a time when Dr. and Mrs. Turner were nearing the end of their service in India: ' Mrs. Turner, a rather stern-looking woman, stood nearby under a large open umbrella, an article she invariably carried, come sunshine or rain.' But, if the Doctor Ammal (Mrs. Turner) looked stern, there is no doubt of the love she was able to inspire in her Indian comrades. ' My dear Dr. and Dr. Ammal,' one of them had written, in welcoming the doctor and his wife back from homeland furlough in 1919, ' My wife and myself sincerely feel glad to hear of your long-expected safe arrival in Nagercoil. . . . We have been simply longing to see you both once more in this land which is so very dear to your hearts. . . . We have been praying with all our hearts to our heavenly Father to keep you from every danger and be pleased to bring you back to us in safety. . . . May God bless you both, and the dear children you have left behind in your homeland. Our many, many head-bowed namaskarams (the graceful ' palms together ' welcoming salutation of the Indian) to you both.'

Mrs. Turner was superintendent of nurses at the time of the Nobles' arrival. ' There were eight trained nurses on the staff, three of them Indian. Captain Mabel Poole, one of the trained nurses, had studied tropical medicine in England. She had come to Nagercoil in 1919, was the pharmacist at the hospital, and when necessary served as midwife.'[13]

' From its early beginnings the Catherine Booth Hospital had a unique reputation for good nursing. At first many of the nurses had only practical training, plus such lectures and instruction in the wards and operating rooms as an overworked staff of doctors could provide from time to time. Nonetheless, both Indian and European patients knew that when they arrived at the Catherine Booth Hospital they would get proper medical and surgical attention, plus excellent and attentive nursing care.'[13]

Mabel Poole, a native of Minehead, England, was training as an officer pupil-midwife at the Mothers' Hospital, Clapton, London, during the First World War when she heard Dr. Percy Turner, who was on homeland furlough from India and was attached to the panel of lecturers and consulting surgeons at the hospital, give a talk to the nurses about the land from which he had just returned and speak of his hopes for the future. The doctor asked for three volunteers who would ' tend Indian patients, win their confidence when they were uncertain of the wisdom of contacting a Christian place of healing, and apply their knowledge of medicine and the message of the gospel '.[17]

When the Matron suggested to Captain Poole that she could render acceptable service in India, therefore, she was ' not wholly unprepared '. An interview with Dr. Turner followed and the young woman committed her life for service overseas. When her studies at the hospital ended she took a course in tropical medicine and in 1919 sailed for Bombay, arriving finally at the Catherine Booth Hospital. There, given the Indian name of Nesammal (Sister of Love), she began the tireless and adaptable service which was to take her not only to several of the branch hospitals, and the beginnings of leprosy nursing at Puthencruz, but also to include periods in the palace of the Maharajah of Travancore, the local potentate, on more than one occasion—once with the special charge of a very sick child of the reigning family.

When, after homeland furlough in 1927, Nesammal returned to India, she was appointed Matron of the Catherine Booth Hospital, a post she held for eleven years. ' Her duties were little different from those of her earlier days at the hospital, though the buildings were larger and the staff increased in number.'[17] It has been recorded of her by a colleague that she had ' amazing skill in complicated maternity cases ' and that ' her very touch seemed to bring healing '.

Following a second period of service in the royal household, Nesammal was appointed in charge of the colony for leprosy sufferers at Puthencruz, in which she had a special interest, and despite a term of missionary service which was lengthened from the then usual seven years to twelve years, because of the outbreak of the Second World War, Mabel Poole's years at the colony were not without happiness. A number of conversions were registered at the corps at Puthencruz and patients became Salvationists. In 1944 came transfer to Koratty, a government colony in the Cochin State run by The Salvation Army, where the Superintendent had charge of 420 leprosy patients—men, women, boys and girls. She ' possessed adaptability to a marked degree ', supervising the growing of grain, root and fruit crops, and learning ' something about electricity, motor cars, building, catering and water supplies '.[17] It was from this centre that, in 1952 as a Brigadier, she retired from active service, to return to her ageing parents in Watchet, Somerset, and to ' continue a life of sacrificial service, seasoned by joyous adventure and motivated by daring abandon to God's will '.[17]

One of the number who was ' trained on the ground ' at the

' C.B.H.' was Brigadier Anna Lautala, who was appointed straight to the hospital from her native Finland, and arrived with little knowledge of even the English language. Very quickly she had gained a good working knowledge of English, as well as the Tamil language, and she soon became a byword for her skill and dependability. Doctors testified that she was ' a tremendously valuable assistant ' in the operating theatre. Following her promotion to Glory, in 1969, the Indian *War Cry* carried a deeply-moving tribute to her written by Mrs. Major Grace Sughanatham, the present out-patient sister at the Catherine Booth Hospital, whose husband is Superintendent of Nurses at the same establishment:

'Brigadier Lautala, widely known and remembered as Retnamoni Ammal, came to India as a missionary in the year 1921. Born in Finland, she was brought up by Lutheran parents but was later attracted to The Salvation Army.

'As a youngster I had the opportunity of knowing the Brigadier while she was working with my parents in various branch hospitals. She was more than a family member to us. She was a hard worker and was loved by the local people for her untiring efforts in serving God. But it is the fellowship we had with her for which I remember her most.

'Again, when I became an officer I had the opportunity of working with the Brigadier in the Catherine Booth Hospital for many years, both in the theatre and in the Eye Block. Retnamoni Ammal was a fully dedicated officer who loved the people who came under her care and moved very closely with them. Much of the Indian way of life was adopted by her, which helped endear her to those she served. She was quick to learn Tamil and was easily understood by all the patients and staff. In those days there were no modern facilities such as we now have in the hospital. Even the most back-breaking of tasks were not avoided by her, and she welcomed hard work. From her example I learned about the dignity of menial labour and the reward of going the second mile—getting as much joy and satisfaction from scrubbing a floor as from helping with an operation. Her teaching of the nurses was by practical demonstration in the wards with little theory taught in the class rooms. For many years she was Colonel (Dr.) Noble's right hand both in the theatre and on the wards.

' Many women officers will remember her and salute her memory and thank God for every remembrance of her service. Her life and devoted service to Christ and the sick to whom she ministered remain with us as an inspiration and a challenge.'

Brigadier Katherine Lord, a trained nurse from Virginia, U.S.A., came as a particular asset to Colonel (Dr.) Wm. Noble when he was setting up a new era in nurse training at the Catherine Booth Hospital, South India, in 1937 by establishing an up-to-date School of Nursing. It was ' a bold and ambitious venture. Few hospitals in India had a qualified nursing school. . . . Few of the young women in India had a high school education or a working knowledge of English. Mohammedan families seldom allowed a daughter to become a nurse, while Brahmin and other high-caste Hindu families feared a breakdown in customs and culture if they permitted a girl to enter into such training '.[13]

Katherine Lord, ' competent and qualified . . . became the first nursing school superintendent.

' In the first class there were eight students. These Indian young people were all Christians, who belonged either to The Salvation Army or other missionary organizations. As the first class progressed other young people were added to the training programme. . . . It was a great milestone when the first R.N. certificates were presented at the Catherine Booth Hospital. . . .

' By 1948 sixty-seven young people had been trained and registered as nurses, and twenty had further qualified as mid-wives. . . . All were a credit to the nursing profession.'[13] In this particular work Katherine Lord ranks as a pioneer. She was promoted to Glory in 1956, having retired from active service in 1952.

England, Canada and the U.S.A. formed the background to the preparation for missionary service of Brigadier Hilda Plummer, a volunteer for leprosy work, whose great love has been the Indian leprosy patients and their children, among whom she has served as an active and retired officer for forty-four years, her only regret being that she has not another forty-four years to give to India and to those with leprosy!

Born in Nottingham, England, to parents who had served as Salvation Army officers, Hilda Plummer had a Primitive Methodist upbringing, her father serving as a local preacher. When she was fifteen her mother died and she went to stay with Salvationists. As a result, a week before emigrating to Canada she was enrolled as a Salvation Army soldier at Nottingham I Corps. It was while in Canada that she heard the testimony of a widowed English officer with four children whose husband had been promoted to Glory from the Far East. She says that it was through this testimony that the desire she had to become a missionary officer became a definite call. Not long afterwards she moved to the U.S.A. and from Troy, N.Y., entered training for Salvation Army officership and volunteered for leprosy work. A year's service as a corps officer was followed by transfer to India.

At the suggestion of Colonel (Dr.) Noble. Hilda Plummer was appointed to the Catherine Booth Hospital for two years. She had had no general nursing training, but the practical experience she gained enabled her to face the challenge of opportunity when she was finally sent to the Cochin State Leprosarium, the government institution of which The Salvation Army, and Dr. Noble in particular, had the oversight.

Leprosy training at Cochin, where she was to spend many years, as well as at Chingleput, where there was a leprosy sanatorium—a Government institution but under Church management—and at Carville, Louisiana, which had the only leprosarium in America, enabled her to give valuable service to the patients and their families; and a first homeland furlough, spent at the Mothers' Hospital, Clapton, in midwifery training, added to her usefulness.

From 1950 to 1960 Brigadier Plummer served as Superintendent in charge of the leprosarium in Bapatla,* a period she regards as the happiest in her life.

'I retired in 1960,' she relates. 'I decided against retiring in my native England or in America. My work was not finished. I had made myself responsible for a healthy girl of leprosy parents . . . so I stayed . . . for her sake. I do not regret my choice.

'I am living in a nice little Indian house in an Indian village. All my neighbours are Indian: some retired officers. One mile south along the railway tracks from where I live is a village of 450 inhabitants. All except the children have leprosy. They have built little huts for themselves and lead normal family life. I help the women before their babies come and when their babies are born. Daily I thank God for giving me this little work for His Kingdom.

'You may wonder if I am happy here. The answer is: Yes, very happy. I may come home one day. I still have joy in *His* service more than all.'

Of Gunvor Eklund, of Sweden, another nurse who has served at the Catherine Booth Hospital, Lieut.-Commissioner (Dr.) Harry Williams has written:

'Gunvor Eklund grew up in the village of Insjön in Dalarna, Sweden. Small though it was, it had a Salvation Army corps.

* See 'Leprosy', p. 144.

From it only one candidate had become a Salvation Army officer (John Hedén, 1896), and he had spent a lifetime in Southern India. Every seven years, except when wars upset the programme, he returned to Sweden on leave . . . and on Lieut.-Colonel Hedén's infrequent furloughs he was invited to speak at the village school. Gunvor sat at her desk lost in wonder. . . . She became the second candidate, but many years were to elapse and there were many hurdles to be jumped before she reached Nagercoil.'[14]

Via the Mothers' Hospital, Clapton, London, Gunvor Eklund came to the Catherine Booth Hospital in South India, where ' she was to tackle a wide variety of tasks . . . but her abiding love has been the leprosy patients. No one can doubt their love for her. Swedish magazines began to publish articles and even collect subscriptions. The matron of her training school heard of her work and moved the trustees of a Memorial Foundation, of which she was president, to allocate funds for leprosy surgery and vocational training of young patients. Slowly the simple and relatively crude wards were transformed, and were always amongst the cleanest in the hospital. They were certainly the happiest, for co-operation and appreciation reach high level among crippled patients. And there was no doubt that she was their " mother " '.[14]

' New Zealand must have the Catherine Booth Hospital engraved on her Salvation Army heart,' wrote Dr. Williams (in 1970), ' for she has sent so many of her sons and daughters to help. None has given more in time and energy than Brigadier Vera Williamson, the Superintendent of Nurses. Unassuming by nature, she was pitchforked into the Matron's office within her first year at the hospital. . . . She has . . . been vigilant in watching the plans of successive Chief Medical Officers to see that due appreciation has been given to nursing needs and problems.

' Her father left the remote Shetland Islands at the age of fifteen. He travelled to Australia alone and in pique. In Australia he found a vigorous Salvation Army and joined it, but it was at Balclutha, in the South Island of New Zealand, that he found a wife from a pioneer family. Two of his daughters became officers.

' Vera says that her call was crystal clear to nursing as well as officership. She holds a diploma in nursing education and administration.* She has been involved in both, serving on the State Nursing Council in its infancy. From all over the world her students write and send her gifts for the Self-Denial Fund. She has no children of her own, but hundreds of the Lord's.'[14]

* See p. 127.

Some Salvationist nurses have had to face the unqualified
opposition of their families at home because of the dedication of
their skills to God in The Salvation Army, and have travelled
overseas without the goodwill of loved ones, often facing a
certain loneliness on arrival at their appointed field of service
because of being the only woman with the qualifications they
hold. Typical of these was Lilian Abel, a ' born ' nurse, who from
Manchester Star Hall entered training to become a Salvation
Army officer from a non-Salvationist background, and sailed for
India in 1932 in the face of strong family disapproval.

Lieutenant Abel's appointment was to the MacRobert Hospital,
Dhariwal, North-Eastern India. Built in 1926 on land leased from
the British India Woollen Mills, and named after the Director of
the time, the hospital was to provide a medical service for the
employees of the mill in return for the lease, as well as serving the
surrounding district. Dr. Samuel Burfoot was the M.O. at the
time, and Nurse Abel the only member of the staff holding S.R.N.
and S.C.M. qualifications. This remained the case until the
arrival, four years later, of Major Margaret Mouat, a devoted
Scottish officer. Lilian Abel afterwards served at the Thomas
Emery Hospital, Moradabad, as Matron from 1939 to 1949,
holding rank as Lieut.-Colonel in the Indian Medical Service in
war years, and being awarded the high honour, Royal Red Cross
(1st Class): Margaret Mouat was to complete $23\frac{1}{2}$ years in
Dhariwal, seeing the hospital grow in capacity from 40 beds to 100
and become a Nurses' Training School under Dr. Harry Williams.

By 1946 Lilian Abel's family had become reconciled to the
fact that she was doing the work to which she had felt called by
God. Today, as a retired Salvation Army Lieut.-Colonel, Lilian
Abel writes: 'I have no regrets. There have been times of
doubting, times of disappointment, but these have been greatly
outweighed by the joy of service and the knowledge that God
was, as I believe, using me—in even a small way—to bring
blessing and help to others. There was always a deep sense of
peace in the assurance that His grace and strength were—and still
are—sufficient for every experience of daily living.'

Africa, as well as India, has had its quota of valiant nurses, and
the story of Brigadier Mary Styles (*Mary of Vendaland*) links this
intrepid officer, awarded The Salvation Army's highest honour—
the Order of the Founder—in 1965, with a warrior-nurse of
earlier times, Major Agatha Battersby, of New Zealand, who
introduced Mary Styles to the people and life she was to make
peculiarly her own in the northern wilds of South Africa.

Dental
surgery
in
São Paulo,
Brazil

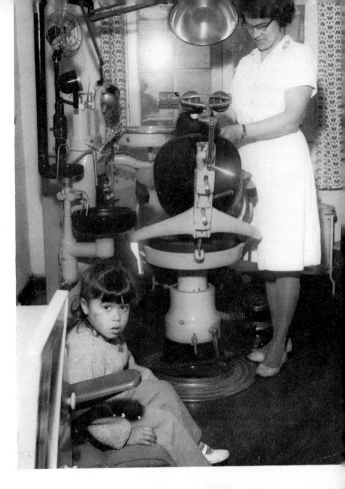

In a rural area, Korea

H.I.H. Princess Chichibu at the opening
of the Booth Memorial Hospital, Tokyo

Dispensary at Moungali,
Brazzaville

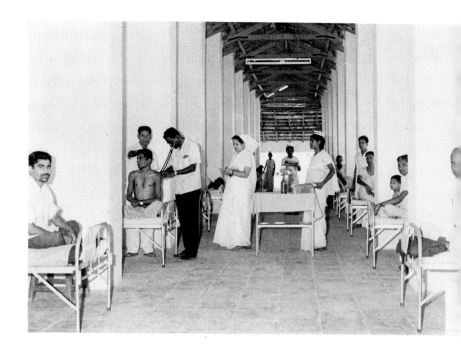

Tuberculosis ward at Ahmednagar,
India

' Bred in the clean white town of Queenstown, in the Cape ', Mary Styles had first made her dedication to God's service in an Anglican Church in Queenstown, when ' listening to an elderly and revered sister speaking about the differing ways in which God called people to His service, and about unexpected places to which they were called.'[18] To her own surprise, Mary found herself declaring, 'And He's called me to be a Salvation Army officer.' At the time she knew little about ' the Army ', except for its open-air meetings, but eventually she became a Salvationist and an officer.

When, as a Lieutenant, she was told she was to be sent to Vendaland she hardly knew where the place was, its location ' tucked away in the extreme northern mountains and plains of South Africa, against the borders of Rhodesia and Portuguese East Africa '.[18] Here The Salvation Army had a settlement, named after William Eadie, one of its early leaders. The District Officer, Adjutant Agatha Battersby, was in charge and Adjutant Mashau, a kindly African, provided male support. The newly-appointed Lieutenant was expected to assist with all that needed to be done, from the cleaning of undergrowth and the making of bricks to assistance with midwifery and the teaching of children to read. Adjutant Battersby was an untiring worker and Mary watched and listened; and learned, as she worked, to cope with clinics, sickness, childbirth and accidents. The main problem at the settlement, part of which was used by the two women as living quarters, was lack of room, in a place that served also as clinic, hospital, hall, classroom and headquarters!

' Successful as a bricklayer, Battersby decided they must have a water tank. Mary learned to use a spade and the tank was made— by digging a hole as large as a room, facing it with bricks and concrete, and then covering the top with zinc sheets which could be removed during rains.'[18]

Besides coping herself with the kind of emergency that arose from a crocodile bite, a mishandled birth, a dental crisis and other demands, on many occasions Mary, with the other two officers as companions, ' would complete a circuit of the district's corps, tramping over the mountains and through the bush—wading rivers and swamps. . . . Sometimes, at night, the party would camp in some remote spot, where Mashau would build a huge fire to scare away unwanted companions '.[18] Wild life abounded in the area!

For eight years Mary lived this wilderness life, before being given opportunity officially to train at Durban for the nursing job to which she had so long been apprenticed. Perhaps it was for this very reason that, having after much toil and application qualified as a nurse and midwife and given service at the Army's hospitals at Cape Town, she began to feel some revulsion at the idea of returning to Vendaland. When orders finally came to do so, she agreed to go ' for a couple of weeks ' but soon found herself deeply involved with the BaVenda (the Venda people) some of whom, remembering her from former days, hailed her return with excited delight, crying, ' The Captain's back! The Captain's back! ' From that moment the BaVenda became her people. It was for her service to them that General Frederick Coutts in 1965 admitted her to the Order of the Founder, the citation declaring: ' Brigadier Mary Styles: has for more than twenty years, from the South Africa Territory's most remote medical station, given devoted care to the BaVenda.'

The William Eadie Settlement became a busy complex of square concrete buildings including the divisional headquarters office, a corps, a hospital clinic and officers' quarters, and her biographer wrote: ' The ambulance Brigadier Mary Styles, O.F., drives is equipped with a gleaming modern stretcher trolley. But when she is descending the giddy crags of the Zoutzpansberg, and tramping the long dusty leagues under the burning Venda skies ', she still finds ' the sack with a couple of poles thrust through is the most practicable way to carry a bulky patient.'[18]

If the people learned to call Mary Styles ' Grandmother ', or ' Mother Styles ', ' the title has none of the disparagement it sometimes carries for Europeans: it is the most dignified title an African woman can receive '. In a farewell tribute to her, when in 1970 Brigadier Mary Styles took leave of those with whom she had worked for so long, the Commissioner General for the Venda and Tsonga ethnic groups wrote:

' In the darkest moments of the lives of many Venda, Brigadier Styles was there to save, to nurse and to serve. Through this work she has built for herself a lasting monument in the hearts of the Venda. I have been struck by the way they, without exception, talk about " Mother Styles ". To them she was a mother in the real sense of the word. . . . I am convinced that the name " Mother Styles " will always be remembered in the greatest gratitude by the Venda.'

In 1950 Ghana was on the verge of independence, the first of the new nations of Africa to emerge from colonial rule. Economically independent, through the boom in cocoa and mahogany, and free of white settlers and colour problems, it was still bound by superstition and ignorance in many aspects of life, and burdened by disease. From the verge of the Sahara in the north came periodic outbreaks of meningitis, brought south by the Hausa cattle dealers. In the forests was bred the tsetse fly with its load of trypanosomes. All over the country were to be found the malaria, tropical ulcers and intestinal diseases that had earned the west coast of Africa its non-welcoming title of 'White Man's Grave'.

Begoro, on an escarpment ninety miles inland from Accra, was a large native town surrounded by cocoa farms and forests rich in mahogany. There The Salvation Army had a large corps, under Captain Benjamin Amu, and a primary school of eight classes under an Australian Lieutenant, Jessie Jenks. It was not The Salvation Army's intention to station a young woman officer alone in a place miles from other Europeans. A married couple, due to arrive at the same time as the Lieutenant, had been unable to come. After a year as the only overseas officer, the Lieutenant received the wonderful news that the first Salvation Army clinic in Ghana was to be opened at Begoro and a nurse was on her way. What excitement in the corps! What rejoicing in the whole town!

On the great day, all the corps, school children and hangers-on marched out to wait for the Divisional Commander's car a mile or so outside the town. From the car emerged a pocket-sized nurse: Captain Agnes Cage. She had served for a time in China and in Korea, but had been flown home for medical treatment. By the time she was ready for duty the door had closed for her return to the Far East. But she willingly agreed to serve in Africa. Triple qualified and experienced, she packed tremendous energy in her small frame. She possessed both a friendly nature and a fierce temper that was to accomplish a great deal when it flared out at shopkeepers selling dangerous drugs bought from pedlars! Because of her almost pure gold hair she was regarded as 'ancient', a source of amusement to the Lieutenant, since the Captain at the time was only thirty or so, but a factor earning her respect from the Africans. This was heightened by the fact that the Chief named her after his grandmother, raising her to high standing in the community.

Now, as she stepped from the car smiling at the crowd, she was ushered to the head of the procession and marched for two or three miles in the tropical midday sun, through the town. The Chief came out on to his dais under the sacred tree in the town's centre. The Presbyterians rang the two big bells in their church tower to show their participation in the general rejoicing. The 'mammy doctor' had come.

There were no materials to start with, save the supplies she had brought with her. The chief loaned a building until the clinic was erected. With a seventeen-year-old girl to translate, the Captain-nurse examined and treated the women and children who came in droves. For a long time no men came. But one day she was called to a house to see a man with pneumonia. In a few days he was up and about again, after being close to death. From then on the ' mammy doctor ' had men as well as women and children on her list.

The maternity cases were the most worrying. The women didn't send for her unless something was wrong. Almost all the summons were night calls, and both officers would be awake as soon as any light was to be seen moving in the village, and be dressed by the time a voice called, 'Agoo! ' outside. That is, the English girl would be dressed, and the 'Aussie' Lieutenant pulled mosquito boots over her pyjama-legs and a dress over her pyjama jacket and insisted that the costume was perfectly in order since it looked all right! Rather green and raw, she went along at night in order to ask the necessary questions and throw out interfering grandmothers! Nothing terrified her more than being given a slimy, choking baby to dangle by the heels, while the nurse coped with the mother, and her fear that she might drop the infant on its head was often shared by the grandmother, who objected to this type of draining and was waiting to carry the naked babe out in the cold night to show it to the father.

One day, the ' mammy doctor ' came to the school, holding a telegram. It was signed ' Leprosy Doctor ' and asked her to assemble leprosy sufferers on a given date. 'Are there any here in the town, or outside? ' she asked. The two women officers went off to their ' very present help ', Captain Amu. ' Yes, there are some in the town and in the farms.'

' But how do I assemble them? I'm not sure I'd recognize one if I saw one.'

' Leave it to me, Captain. I'll ask the Chief to beat the talking drum, and everyone will know.'

So once more the problem was left in Captain Amu's capable hands. The women officers heard the drum beating. Its message, unintelligible to them, was obeyed; and when the Government doctor arrived the patients were there. Was ' Sister ' willing to hold a leprosy clinic and issue DADPS and check reactions? ' Sister ' expressed herself willing but ignorant. So for several hours the sweating pair examined patients together, the doctor explained symptoms and side-effects and the sister listened and learned. From then on the sufferers came regularly for their treatment.

Another day it was the local policeman who arrived. A man had cut his throat. Would sister come and write out a medical report?

'Is he dead?'

'No, but soon to die,' was the reply in the West Coast pidgin. Salvation Army Captains do not use bad language to police constables. Let us say a kind of snarl slipped out as 'mammy doctor' snatched up bandages and raced to the police post. The man was still alive when she had finished her first aid. She sent for a local truck driver. He was unenthusiastic about taking the man twenty-five miles to hospital: he would surely die and haunt the lorry. Then the Captain, who had been gently dripping milk into the man's mouth, paused in her labour of love and drew herself up to her full 'five feet nothing' and blazed. In a little while, a terrified policeman was instructing the cringing driver to get his patient to the hospital with every care and diligence. Hangers-around were fading into the background with all speed, while the Captain enlarged on the topic of the report she would be sending if . . .

A few weeks later the man returned with his throat neatly healed, and the 'mammy doctor' was greeted with even more veneration than before. The children loved her. They could not understand, of course, what she said to the mothers who tried to cure baby's cold by stuffing red pepper in its ears and nostrils.

On Saturday mornings the two women officers wandered through the village shops and market, buying a tin of fish here and some bananas there, but in actual fact keeping an eye open to see what medicines were on sale. Pilfering from Government hospitals was not uncommon and 'M and B 693' was regarded as a cure-all. After a fight to save the Chief's wife, who had taken an overdose in blissful ignorance, the 'mammy doctor' was on the look-out for the source. This led to the Saturday rambles through the shops, the two usually escorted by a group of small children. One woman rebuked a little tot for clinging to the Captain's white skirt with grubby hands. Proudly the tot replied, 'When I go to the clinic, she sits me on her knee.'

The story is one without an end, for it is a recurring one in different places, with different people still needing a 'mammy doctor' to love, bully and cajole them.

Emilia van Hoogstraten was already a fully-trained nursing sister when, from the Netherlands, she entered The Salvation

Army's International Training College in London in 1932. Possessed of a burning spirit of evangelism, she found her first appointment—to the training college staff, for service in the health lodge—severely chafing to her ardent spirit with its desire to be ' out among the people ' and working for the poorest and most needy. She discovered means of fulfilling her longings, however, in the surrounding Camberwell district and would be off alone, whenever her duties permitted, to seek out and help the poor and churchless of the area.

Returning to her native Netherlands, she was given an appointment nearer to her heart, though several times, while engaged in midnight work, her life was in peril. Danger was to be a recurring factor in Emilia's service as an officer-nurse. She was stationed in her own country when, in 1940, the German military breakthrough occurred and the Dutch training college was quickly turned into a first aid post. For a period she nursed the wounded day and night, a strong physique serving her well in the crisis. Later she was appointed to Belgium and, hearing from returning missionary officers of the great needs of the Congo, volunteered for that field.

Though not brought up as a Salvationist, Emilia van Hoog-straten breathes naturally, what is known in the Movement as ' the Army spirit '. In a personal letter, written from Equatorial Africa following a time of political upheaval and heavy fighting in the early 1960's, she described something of her experiences: ' You know that during the September war I was in Katanga. There was very much to do for the wounded. I tried to do what I could for them, spiritually and materially. There was very great suffering in the four town hospitals (Elisabethville) . . .' Some of the patients she tended had encountered unspeakable horrors.

A report to International Headquarters said: ' Elisabethville has been cut off from the rest of the territory for months but Brigadier E. van Hoogstraten has worked with great devotion amongst her people.'

Having to cross the border to Ndola (then in Northern Rhodesia) for supplies just before Christmas, Brigadier van Hoogstraten found herself unable to get back to Katanga, as fighting had broken out in the area. ' I could not go back,' she wrote; ' I could only help the thousands of refugees who came through.' The modest statement covered a period of strenuous and often heart-breaking activity.

On her return to Elisabethville, she was to write: ' The Salvation Army is the first mission to be back in town and the

Katangan soldiers at the border cheered me. "The Salvation Army is back! Good! Good!" they called out.' Her reception by her own African comrades was deeply moving. Going immediately to the largest of the corps, she was joyfully reunited with her friends. ' You should have seen them,' she wrote. ' There was dancing and rejoicing. I felt like a mother coming home to her children.' She never failed to pay tribute to the courage of her African comrades, and her account of the African officer who made his way through the firing in the streets to make contact with her would bring the tears to her eyes as she recalled the incident.

Soon after this, she found herself distributing relief and acting as padre and goodwill officer, as well as divisional officer. But every added responsibility was joyfully borne for the sake of the people she was serving. ' I thank the Lord every day for placing me here,' was her testimony. To friends in Europe her only request was for a continuance of prayer on her behalf. ' It is so strengthening to know that you, with many others, are praying for me,' she told them. ' There is nothing like prayer: it is the strongest weapon in our warfare.' She was referring, of course, to the spiritual battle the Salvationist constantly wages.

When the official time came for her retirement, Emilia van Hoogstraten was—as might be imagined—reluctant to leave the African comrades with whom she had so closely identified herself, but a period of residence in Marseilles, where she was able to develop a ministry of her own to African seamen in this cosmopolitan port, helped her to feel she was still serving her beloved Africa, albeit from across the sea. A largely unsung heroine, Emilia is typical of many nurses whose service has been unstintingly given in the missionary field, above and beyond the call of duty.

Chapter
Two

IN A NEAR-
STONE-AGE WORLD

PAPUA/NEW GUINEA—' The Last Unknown '—is the eastern half of a large island north of Australia. The western half, known as West Irian, is a part of Indonesia, but the Territory of Papua/ New Guinea, moving toward self-government, is at present administered by Australia. It has the problems—present and potential—of any developing country. The tropical coast is half a century ahead of the mist-shrouded Highlands, where bark-string skirts are more common than western clothes and where illiteracy is normal and fear and superstition are dominant. Belief in sorcery and black magic is widespread. The principal welfare services are provided by the respective departments of health and by the missions.

The Salvation Army opened its work in this region in 1956. Though many missions and churches are active here, large areas of the Highlands are almost untouched so far as evangelical, medical and educational work are concerned. The Administration is happy to have the help of the missions in the two last-named fields. So it was that the Government accepted the offer of The Salvation Army's help in the Highlands of New Guinea at *Kainantu*, and, in 1958, Captain Ruby Dalrymple and Lieutenant Dorothy Elphick began work there, first carrying out infant welfare work in their car-shed, and then in the villages in a thirty mile radius, as well as caring for maternity cases and children suffering from malnutrition at the adjacent government hospital. Later a clinic was built on the ' mission plot ', allotted to The Salvation Army, next to the hospital and, eventually, the in-patient work was handed over to the hospital staff.

One of the roadside clinics established was at *Onamuga*, a Salvation Army ' mission station ', twenty-two miles away where, when the officers first undertook a monthly clinic, they stayed overnight. In 1965, Captain Elphick was appointed to Onamuga and further extended the scope of the medical work during her brief stay of eight weeks. With two indigenous nurses from the coast, she visited the villages and encouraged the people to attend for treatment. Mrs. Captain Donald Gates took up this work after Captain Elphick moved. Over the years the names of Mrs. Captain Gates, Captains Dorothy Elphick, Beulah Harris, Bette Sampson and Beryl Robinson, and Sisters Vera Koch and Gwen Oates have earned respect and affection in the villages around the station.

In 1966, two New Zealand nurses, Captains Dorothy Elphick and Beryl Robinson, were appointed to the Goverment Rural Health Centre, *Henganofi* District, with its twelve aid posts, and the oversight of a population of 35,000. The Salvation Army had offered to help there for a period of three years. Certain limitations were placed on the evangelical work of the officer-nurses but no human agency can limit the influence of a godly life and character. This work ended in 1969.

Sogeri Clinic, situated some thirty-two miles from Port

Moresby—on the Kokoda Trail, of war-time renown—fulfils a valuable service. Sister Gwen Peterson commenced this work for The Salvation Army in 1964. It was carried on by Mrs. Captain Gates, Mrs. Major William Mole and, more recently, by Mrs. Captain Stanley Evans. The clinic serves many small villages and plantation workers. Many of the people walk along the trail some fifteen miles to receive attention, and of these some are frequently taken to Port Moresby if their condition demands it.

The newest development in Salvation Army medical work in the Highlands is at *Misapi*, of which more later.

*　　*　　*

Who can say who does the nobler work—Sister A—who carries on with the routine work day after day in an established mission station, or Sister B—who goes out pioneering alone in untrodden ways, braving loneliness, landslides and leeches? One has more home comforts, the other has more interest, excitement, and perhaps more prayer support. Both are equally necessary to the welfare of the people and to the work of God's Kingdom. As one reads of the pioneering nurse, therefore, one must not forget the others carrying on the routine work in the established centres.

*　　*　　*

Dorothy Elphick grew up on a farm in the ' backblocks ' of New Zealand. Her parents, good-living people of pioneer stock, were not particularly religious, and during the Depression there was not a lot of money to spend on long drives to church. But, when a neighbour called for them, the children were allowed to go to Sunday-school. When she was only three or four years old, Dorothy heard a missionary, home from South America, speak at the Sunday-school and decided to be a missionary when she grew up.

At sixteen she went as a nurse-aid in a hospital close to Auckland. Here she fell in with a gay crowd of girls and was enjoying the delights of ' Vanity Fair ' when a Christian nurse, newly arrived on transfer, chanced to say she had no one to go to church with her. Quite lightheartedly Dorothy offered to keep her company, not really expecting the ' senior ' to accept. But off they went, and Dorothy was rather taken aback when her new friend took her to The Salvation Army because the corps officer was a friend.

As she listened to the speaker, all the bits and pieces the young nurse-aid had heard in religious instruction at school, and in her occasional attendances at Sunday-school, seemed to click into

place. The historical Christ became the Saviour dying on the
Cross for her sins; and there, in her seat, she accepted His salvation. Although her friend was not a Salvationist, the two nurses
were often at the corps because the officers opened their home to
them. They began a Nurses' Christian Fellowship at the hospital.
Later, at an Easter Convention, Dorothy heard clearly and defi-
nitely the call to missionary service.

The years of nursing training and qualification went by and
were followed by entry into the Salvation Army college for
training as an officer. Here Dorothy made no secret of her wish
to serve in the Highlands of New Guinea as a missionary nurse,
and her dreams were to be vividly fulfilled.

*What is the life of a nurse like in the near-Stone-Age environment of
the New Guinea Highlands?* The following description is from the
pen of the pioneering Captain Elphick herself and describes
conditions in 1958–59 at *Kainantu*:

' We don't have to take any notice of you—after all you are
only women! What difference if you are white?' So replied a
surly New Guinean to the two officer-nurses when they advised
hospital treatment for his child, who was suffering from malnutrition. The very idea of going through his enemies' ground
and then staying in a large building with a ' copper' roof—for
how long?—dismayed him. Someone would be sure to ' work
poison' on him, his number three wife and the child. One just
couldn't tell what else would be likely to happen, and so far from
the home village! What if the child should die? Its spirit would
not be in the right area. Oh, the horror of such a suggestion!

' If you don't go and get your " somethings " and come along
with us to the Kainantu hospital for the doctor to see your son,
he will die and we will have to report this to the *kiap* (Government
Patrol Officer),' was the sisters' significant threat.

'Ah, what a laugh! To think we are going to listen to the
white women!' And off he went into the bush, up the hill.

' How did your roadside clinics go this trip, Sister?' the
Medical Orderly at the hospital casually inquired as a sick man
was unloaded into his care. The story was briefly recounted. Two
days out, driving up and down the very narrow road, over even
narrower rickety wooden bridges, getting stuck in a muddy patch,
or having to wait for a truck to be dug out of a ' slip '. Of course
these are ' the everyday things in life ' in this developing country.
But the trying incident of seeing a child snatched away from
medical care and taken into the darkness of the old village ways!
That was too much.

The names of the parents and child were given, and later an indigenous policeman was detailed to bring them into the hospital. For these village people such action was quite unanticipated. That white women could, or would, do such a thing—and they of a Christian mission! But how else would the parents learn?

A short time spent by the miscreants in the government hospital, close to the nursing sisters' home, gave these reluctant inhabitants time and opportunity to observe the ways of the two women responsible for their present temporary absence from their village. There they frequently saw them, in and out of the hospital at all hours of the day and night, giving bottles of milk to some very tiny children—some so thin they could not stand up. Often the big white vehicle was away for a night, and the two women would be going around villages in another part of the country.

* * *

During six years in that appointment changes were noted by the nursing sisters. Many things entered the villages to improve life there. Coffee grown in village plots brought improved economy, and whilst there was plenty of money the family had plenty of tinned fish or meat; the health of whole families improved as the vitally needed protein was obtained. This, in turn, has emptied many hospital beds of severe malnutrition cases—kwashiorkor patients.

* * *

' Whatever has been happening down there?' was the question asked of Captain Beulah Harris, who had returned home from the hospital very late one night.

' Oh, I've been put through the third degree about spiritual things. The doctor has been questioning me. He's seeking after the spiritual life, but says it's so simple he can't accept it.'

' He wants to put it in a test-tube, eh?'

Assisting in a practical way as well as giving moral support to the one doctor at the government hospital next door added interest to the nurses' field of clinical work, as they gave a hand where and when needed. Their lives were being watched. Did they live out what they professed?

Captain Harris excelled not only in explaining the reason for her faith in the Great Physician, but the medical and one hundred and one other tasks always crying out for attention at *Kainantu*. Sometimes the ' morning' town clinic ran over into the early afternoon, and the home leaguers waited patiently for their meeting. A corps programme, as well as the village clinical work, left the busy officers little time to get bored.

*   *   *

'Would you mind coming down to the theatre, please, Sister? I have what I think could be a — but as I've never seen one before I thought you, with your experience at Crown Street Hospital, might have.' The young, inexperienced doctor, new to the land and many of the medical problems, was not so proud that he couldn't recognize when some woman might have seen or experienced more of one particular kind of ailment than he had. Lieutenant Beryl Cunningham needed no second glance to advise him to evacuate the patient to the Base Hospital at Goroka, where there were better facilities to deal with major surgery.

*   *   *

The scene is *Onamuga*.

'I don't think this child will last very much longer. He's nearly dead now.'

Captain Donald Gates offered prayer, after some injections had been given. On the nurses' return from meetings in nearby villages, the child was found to be no worse or better—but, amazingly, still alive. Maybe worth the two-hour drive into Kainantu? 'There's a slip on the road which won't be cleared until tomorrow at the earliest,' came the Captain's voice. 'Well, while there's life there's hope,' remarked Mrs. Gates.

The government medical aid post, across the stream by the station, had been closed for some weeks. Monday morning clinic was the nurses' only official medical service, apart from the two days, weekly, around surrounding villages. There was nowhere in the vicinity for the sick to sleep, and those like this prostrate child needed to be near the 'medicine house' and the sister. All afternoon, constant care was given to him in the old bush hut which served as a clinic. By dark, the cold wind—cutting up through well-spaced rough-sawn floor boards—made life miserable. (At over 6,000 feet above sea level, even in the tropics it can be rather cold at night.)

'They're asleep now. I'll stay and watch him. You had better go and get some shut-eye. There's clinic in the morning, and you'll need to be awake for that.' No one disagreed with Sister Gates as she gave another dropperful of liquid to the barely conscious child. The parents watched in sullen silence as a friend put another stick on the fire in the round house all had moved into. (It was really the cookhouse the carpenter had used when

he had camped in a bush-house close by, while building the
teacher's house.)

*That was how the Salvation Army medical aid post work began in
the area.* It seemed that the story was echoed around the hills that
the ' dead ' child had been prayed over and worked on all night
before being taken into Kainantu when the road had opened. He
had returned home alive and well. Somehow, there were other
sick ones who needed three or four-hourly treatment. They had
it from two triple-certificated nursing sisters. When one was out,
the other oversighted the in-patients.

*   *   *

The scene changes again, this time to *Henganofi*.

' Three years—from the 2nd of February, 1966, to the 3rd of
February, 1969—of looking after a government rural health
centre of thirty beds and twelve medical aid posts with a population of 35,000, brought many and varied experiences to Captain
Beryl Robinson and me,' wrote Captain Elphick.

Captain Beryl looked at the young woman lying unconscious
on the village green, as the frightened villagers crowded round.
Another case of ' poison ' having been ' worked on ' the victim
by a sorcerer? He could have been paid to do this by someone
wishing revenge on her, or one of her family. What to do with,
or for, such a case, was the problem. What could be done for her
at the health centre? She would surely die if left in her present
environment. As the unhappy onlookers wanted her taken to
Kainantu hospital, yes, the officer decided that would please them
and solve a problem beyond her experience.

Fortunately the young Australian doctor at the hospital was
not unfamiliar with such cases; his experience in other Territory
centres helped him to understand when the Henganofi health
centre vehicle pulled up outside the hospital office. There could
have been some embarrassing moments for the Captain otherwise,
as the patient was sitting up enjoying a piece of sweet potato!
The doctor kept the patient in hospital a few days and treated the
many minor sores she had, then allowed her to walk home. ' This
type of episode is not an uncommon one in the land,' writes
Captain Elphick. ' The power of the forces of fear, used in this
evil manner, makes one realize how dark is the life to which many
are in bondage. It is only the Light of the World who can break
their fetters. Ours is the task of being His hands, feet and mouth-
piece whilst granted days upon this earth.'

Nurses are people too, of course. They come in a variety of

shapes and sizes and temperaments, and from differing backgrounds. What is a cross to one may not weigh at all heavily on
another. Fun-loving and vivacious Captain Bette Sampson came
from a big family and town. One could picture her in a large
corps with lots of young life around her—timbrels and guitars
and drama groups, very likely. Yet for three years she nursed at
Onamuga, isolated from the youth of her own culture but giving
herself to the people of New Guinea.

Sister Gwen Oates came from a country town in Victoria,
Australia. One would probably choose adjectives like ' calm '
and ' soothing ' rather than ' vivacious ' to describe her temper-
ment, though she also enjoyed outings and picnics and having
visitors. Her particular cross was driving on the mountainous
roads, often slippery after rain, to hold roadside clinics or to fetch
patients.

Another thorn in the flesh—to all nurses in these primitive
areas—is the habit of patients departing without permission, as
soon as they feel better. This is particularly galling when a
mother takes a sick child home at a stage when the nurse knows
that further care and treatment are essential.

' Strangely enough, I have never heard a nursing sister complain of the *conditions* under which she worked,' writes Captain
Elphick. ' She might have an occasional moan about the vehicles
or the roads, or the lack of understanding shown by the relatives
of a patient, or even about living with other workers of different
temperament or age. But the smoke-grimed *haus-sik* with its
earth floor, smoky cooking fire, and bamboo beds firmly planted
in the floor, has been accepted without a murmur. True, visiting
" high-up " officers from Australian, English and Canadian backgrounds, were taken to see it in all its glory and told casually that
a small hospital ward with a cement floor and glass windows
would be easier to work in and keep clean. And in time Onamuga
saw such an innovation, but the sterile hospital atmosphere
would have terrified the villagers a few years ago, whereas the
haus-sik was more like home to them.'

Life for a nurse is often a blend of comedy and tragedy. It
demands great fortitude and emotional stability if the nurse is not
to be ' torn to shreds ' in her own spirit.

How great is the strain, however, for a lone nurse who has to
diagnose without all the aids available at a hospital! And, under
her training and discipline, she is still a woman at heart. Was
Sister Gwen described as calm? Yet, there she is in a corner of
the deserted clinic, sobbing her heart out over the death of a little

brown baby—brought to her too late—for whose life she has battled for several days.

At other times the sister needs a sense of humour to help her over the less refined incidents in which her work involves her. As when her medical orderly informs her *he has put an arrow into a man*, one of a group lurking near the clinic in the dark, whom he suspects of 'working poison'! The men ran away (who could blame them?), but he knows he has hit one—the broken shaft, but not the head of the arrow, is there.

Paragraphs from Captain Elphick's pen portray some of her experiences during the first twelve years at Kainantu, Onamuga and Henganofi, where she strove to be *both nurse and missionary*. 'For which is of more value: a living body or a living soul?' she asks. But always the urge was upon her to pioneer. 'Some are called and fitted to be pioneers, to face loneliness and primitive conditions—and others are called and fitted to build on their foundations, to develop and consolidate. How wonderful is the diversity of God's gifts and His use of varied talents and temperaments!'

*   *   *

Early in May, 1970, Captain Elphick received permission from her headquarters in Sydney to go out and explore the Gimi area of the Papua/New Guinea region and consider possible centres of activity. In a not-very-new vehicle loaded with camping gear, she set out alone from Onamuga and drove to Okapa—a Government patrol post with a small hospital—and then beyond. The road wound up and down and around the mountains, with room for only one vehicle in many parts and steep drops into the valleys at one side of the road.

An Australian *War Cry* report (July 18, 1970) said of the area: 'It is full of difficulties and dangers, as much from the people as the terrain. Some tribes in the area are cannibal and the eating of the human brain by the women folk has caused a disease that has killed many of them. The men are in a three to one ratio to the women.'

One of the Captain's main concerns was to find out what work other missions proposed to do in Gimi and what their attitude would be to her arrival. At a New Tribes mission station she found a warm welcome and every offer of assistance. Leaving her car in the care of the missionaries, she walked on to *Misapi*, a Gimi village, whose headman she had met some weeks earlier in Okapa and where she had sent her camping gear the day before. The three-hour walk took her through several small villages and some bush, and over a swinging cane bridge. As night came on, bringing heavy rain, the men of the village gathered in the house to talk to her. They had already marked a piece of land for ' mission use ' for they said other places had a *haus-lotu* and they had no place of worship. They would like her to stay. As she had not mentioned to any of them that she was a nurse, the Captain was impressed by their hunger for the gospel. While rain poured down outside, she talked with them for more than two hours, telling them what The Salvation Army's principles and beliefs were.

On the Tuesday, Captain Dorothy again set out on foot to explore other villages. A mud track up a steep hill and through bush was too slippery for her and one boy went ahead with a spade, cutting steps; two men held her arms and a line of small boys followed with her kitbag, lamp, kettle and the traditional string bag, or *billum*. At the tail of the procession was a sick woman, and a second woman helping her, on the way to a government aid post. They crossed a river on a single log and, after five hours of walking, reached Paiti. This centre of habitation consisted of twenty-four houses strung along a ridge, and the aid post. The Captain was given a house to stay in and at 6 p.m. she held a meeting to explain her presence. By 8 p.m. she was in bed, ' tired but happy in the Lord ' and not unduly disturbed by the village noises—excited talk, dogs, pigs and fowls.

The next day she visited the aid post and the village of Somai, on her way back to Misapi. The following day she again went out exploring. Leaving Misapi at 9 a.m., she followed a slippery track through the bush, picking hungry leeches off her bare legs and feet at intervals; along the top of a ridge, along a road— so called—through cloud and mist, to arrive in the gathering darkness at the home of another lone woman missionary, a friend of many years. This was a walk of ten and a quarter hours and the Captain was ' too tired to eat or talk much '. She washed off the mud and blood from leech bites and crawled into bed.

*   *   *

As a result of Captain Elphick's report on this trip, The Salvation Army instructed her to go down to Misapi on a trial basis. The government Regional Medical Officer expressed himself delighted to have her working there.

On her return to Misapi in June, the Captain revealed her medical qualifications, and a village shop was put at her disposal for a temporary clinic, while she continued to live in the grass-roofed house with an earth floor, sleeping on a camp bed, cooking on an open fire and washing in a baby's bath.

The day begins with prayers for all the villagers who care to come. Then the sick are treated, after which the Captain goes down from the village to the ' mission station ' to oversee the clearing, fencing and building. There has to be built—of local materials—a clinic, a ward, a house for herself, and a hall for worship. (A landing strip is high on the list of priorities.) A fence to keep out pigs must be built before a garden can be planted. When one starts with a site covered with reeds ten feet high, and a volunteer work force with a minimum of hand tools— no bulldozers or cranes to ease the task—the work does not go forward speedily. *But the Captain will see it through.*

Here, in her own words, are her comments on the first seven weeks of her official appointment there:

> The challenge in the needs of a smaller group of people, in an isolated area like Misapi, places more dependence upon the Great Physician . . . forty mountainous miles from the nearest doctor—if the road is open— or four or five hours' hard drive up. A valuable lesson learnt in other places is proving its worth: '*When you've done your human best for the sick, pray and leave the rest to God. He knows and understands.*' The spiritual opportunities can be used at such times to turn the sufferer, and relations and onlookers, to the great Sin-bearer.
>
> The knowledge that there are people in many places upholding a servant of the Lord is a great comfort and encouragement—especially when things are not going as well as they might be, or one thinks they should be.

*　　　*　　　*

The story must end there. It is ' the end of the beginning '. Let us leave our valiant nurse with her malaria cases and sick babies and men with arrow wounds, building up a little bit of the Kingdom of God in Misapi.

Chapter
Three

OVER THE HILLS AND FAR AWAY

KULAWI is a delightfully situated municipality nestling in the midst of a vast mountainous tract, consisting of about thirty-two villages and a population of over 20,000 scattered over a vast area; the headmen of over twenty of these villages are Salvationists (writes Major Estelle Kjelson, a Canadian-trained nurse, from Sulawesi-Tengah, Indonesia). Salvation Army missionary officers commenced preaching and teaching the gospel in what was then Celebes over fifty years ago, as well as providing simple medical aid to the numerous people they contacted.

In 1949, a clinic was opened in Kulawi and a more vigorous attempt was made to provide health services to the community. Four years later a similar clinic was opened in the village of Kantewu (about seventy miles further into the mountains) with an officer solely responsible for health services to the surrounding villages. Both these clinics ceased operating in the late 1950's, due to the local political situation and lack of medical staff.

During the visit of the Territorial Commander for Indonesia in 1963, a delegation approached him requesting that the poli-clinic be re-established in Kulawi. By this time the former building was unsatisfactory, and the Territorial Commander therefore suggested that the local people should erect a new clinic and living quarters and he would send an officer with medical supplies, when this project had been completed. The people commenced enthusiastically to gather the necessary materials from the surrounding jungle, but their efforts soon stagnated as there was no officer to spur them on. At that time I was in charge of The Salvation Army's William Booth Hospital in Surabaja, Djawa, and an officer from Sulawesi wrote me of their plight. I spoke to the Territorial Commander and offered to arrange my time so that I could take six weeks off to come to Kulawi, with two national nurses (trained in our Surabaja Hospital) and re-establish the work here. We brought medical supplies and some furnishings from Surabaja.

After a hectic journey of ten days on an inter-island freighter—the four of us with medicines and our personal belongings sand-wiched in a small 'cabin' we managed to rent from a crew member—we eventually arrived in the port of Donggala. Our baggage, to my dismay, was transported by small, fragile skiffs to shore and a waiting truck, which then conveyed us over rough roads and through several streams to Palu, the capital city of this province, where the Salvation Army Divisional Headquarters is located. Here we visited the Government doctor, to obtain the necessary permits to re-open our work in Kulawi. This was readily given and, in addition, the doctor loaned us his four-wheeled 'drive' to bring us to Kulawi. That was something of a sensational journey of seventy miles! We arrived in Kulawi to be confronted by a half-completed clinic. Our time was limited, so we called the local people and told them we had ten days before the official opening! They rallied to the challenge and in the latter part of August 1964, with the Government doctor, provincial and local officials present, the William Booth Clinic was re-opened to provide health services to the hundreds of people in this vast area.

I remained for three days with the girls, to get them organized. During that period over 400 people visited the clinic, besides our making several house-calls. One patient seriously ill with typhoid fever was transported several miles, hoping for admission to the clinic. This proved to be impossible, but he was nursed in a nearby house until he regained his health, and this made a great impression on the community.

In spite of my short stay, I visited the former clinic in Kantewu where—surprisingly after an interval of ten years—the medical supplies left behind were still found to be usable. *En route* we conducted clinics in several villages, and a couple followed me back to Kulawi to have some aching teeth extracted! During these five days we had walked nearly 200 miles, so we arrived back hobbling on swollen and blistered feet, as they were not accustomed to these rough, stony mountain paths. I returned to my task in Surabaja with the medical needs of this area imprinted on my mind and heart!

Following homeland furlough, I came to Kulawi in December 1966, with medical supplies for two years. The manner in which these supplies were transported to Kulawi is a story in itself. Suffice to say that, with the co-operation of the officer in charge of the Salvation Army Maternity Clinic in Makassar, we erected a storage room, thirty feet by nine feet, and the day the ship with nine and a half tons of medical supplies for Kulawi arrived in Makassar, the last door was being put on the storage room! I knew there was no place in Kulawi to store the goods, so I had taken eighty boxes with me; and the rest was left in Makassar, where it remained for a year, giving us time to erect storage buildings in Kulawi.

Indeed, we were faced now with a challenging task of establishing a more permanent footing for our medical work in the province of Sulawesi-Tengah.

In 1967 we set out to visit some of the remoter villages to conduct services and clinics. Our convoy consisted of ten horses, and this trek lasted nearly a month. After the first hundred miles we travelled on foot, the supplies being transported by carriers! Over one torrential river I was ' piggy-backed ' by a teacher. The ' bridge ' was a tree-trunk and the one consolation was that if he slipped, we fell in together! At each village *en route* we conducted clinics, sometimes working far into the night by a flickering light, as many of the people had been waiting so long for our arrival.

By the time we arrived at the village about twenty miles from Kulawi, we called for fresh reinforcements to conduct the clinic there, and I came on home, minus several toe nails!

In October of the same year, we were asked to reopen the Kantewu clinic. In spite of the fact it had been vacant for so many years, with simple renovations it was possible for it to be re-occupied. At the request of the Regional Head—that it be re-opened on November 12, following the remembrance services which were being held in that village—we had exactly a week to get the place organized and on November 12, 1967, the clinic was officially reopened, the District Officer, the Regional Head, and representatives from the Military, the Department of Health, and the heads of all the surrounding villages being present. A note in my diary runs: ' Today we have opened what is very likely the most primitive clinic in The Salvation Army; no sanitation facilities, no water, the nearest river about half a mile away.' At the request of the local people, the centre has been named ' Woodward ', in memory of Lieut.-Colonel Leonard Woodward, who pioneered the evangelical work in that area.

Today we have a well. Eleven sacks of cement were carried over the sometimes almost impassable mountain trails. It is the first well in the area and what a blessing it is, when I visit the clinic, to enjoy a bath from this fresh, clean water. The clinic is directly under the supervision of Kulawi, the national nurses rotating for service, two or three months at a time. It is a big responsibility for them: there have been over five thousand new patients since the day it was reopened, and some twenty thousand treatments have been given, besides the many visits made to the other villages.

On one of these trips the national nurse suffered an acute attack of bacillary dysentry. She was unconscious for several hours and was carried to Kantewu by the friendly villagers. When the news reached me, I left immediately for Kantewu. On my arrival she had regained her strength.

In the early part of 1968 we visited several villages near the border between South and Central Sulawesi, conducting clinics and sleeping wherever there was a place to lay my head. Even if the roof leaked, the raincoat made a good covering! That same year we journeyed to a district east of Palu and, as the place is not in this municipality, having obtained special permission from the Department of Health, we spent two weeks in the area, treating people by the hundreds. Before our departure a delegation asked us to open a clinic there also. Steps were taken to fulfil their request, and it should have been commenced last year, but the officer appointed fell ill, and so for the time being they must wait.

In 1969 I did less travelling and concentrated on our building projects in Kulawi. We began by completely renovating and enlarging our living quarters into a more permanent structure. In August the special dedication service was conducted by the Divisional Commander, on the erection of the framework of the new hospital and clinic. This project was wholly constructed by local labour. With the assistance of a candidate for officership and one of the girls, together we laid all the pipes and connected all the taps. (We have plastic pipes for fresh water from a reservoir set on a spring in the mountain.) Only as one realizes the circumstances here does one appreciate the miraculous fact that a hospital for fourteen patients, nine 'general' and five maternity beds, and an out-patients' clinic was completed in less than a year. On July 30, 1970, the Provincial Resident (representing the Governor) officially opened the hospital and health centre. The dedication service was conducted by the Territorial Commander. To quote from a report made at the time: 'Representatives of the provincial and local Governments, besides the Doctor, head of the Provincial Health Department, were loud in their praises of this structure completed to the benefit of the community.' Thus the Salvation Army Health Centre, Bethesda (*Hou Popkaria*), Kulawi, officially opened its doors to admit anyone requiring in-patient care.

Our first patient was a local merchant, seriously ill with typhoid fever. After a month he had made a complete recovery. Since then several patients from outlying villages have slowly come to understand the advantage of in-patient care. More than 10,000 new patients have visited the out-patient clinic, and a similar number have been treated in other villages or their homes. These have been a 'busy' three-and-a-half years! In spite of hazardous journeys over mountain tracks, physical fatigue and a few bouts of malaria, I can testify to the grace and goodness of God. He called me: He has been faithful. And I am indebted to my Indonesian assistants, who have worked long and hard hours by my side. Most of them come from Djawa, and it is no easy matter for them either, for all our home visits are done on foot or on horseback.

When we recently sent a midwife and assistant to Kantewu, the midwife, who was fulfilling her first spell of duty there, rode one of my horses and the boy candidate assistant had charge of another loaded with medical supplies. Once, the consignment

fell off and the horse raced for home, but fortunately was re-
captured. After reloading they again had to unload to cross a
river where the bridge had earlier been swept away. This meant
reloading again, of course, on the far side. Relating the incident,
the poor lad told me that many times he had nearly cried, but then
had thought what was the use of crying—he had no pain! Eventually they arrived at the village where they were to change
horses, and we discovered we had loaded on to one horse what
really should have been loaded on to two! Are there other clinics,
I wonder, where the only mode of travel is on horseback or by
foot?

Chapter
Four

HOW FAITH AND
WORKS BUILT A
HOSPITAL

CANADIAN born Mrs. Lieut.-Colonel Leonard Kirby, formerly
Isobel Stoman, of Brantford, Ontario, and Brigadier Ruth
Hacking, a Lancashire lass, were both qualified nursing sisters
when in 1948 their Salvation Army service brought them together
in Rhodesia: the former as the wife of the district officer, Senior-
Captain Kirby, whose parents had themselves been Brantford
Salvationists before becoming redoubtable missionary officers in
Central Africa, and the latter newly arrived from England to serve
as nurse in charge of the dispensary at Mbembeswana, then the
locale of the headquarters for the Semokwe District.

A retired Swiss officer, Brigadier Gertrud Wackernagel,
describes conditions as she knew them in the 1930's at Mbembeswana, in that region of sandy, thorny desert:

> The dispensary proper, as well as the little quarters, each had a large
> water tank of galvanized iron with a tap and padlock. In periods of
> drought when only a small supply of water was left and carefully hoarded
> for further emergencies, we managed to get extra water from the pump
> of a Government cistern, whence an African comrade brought supplies
> in a petrol drum on an ox-cart daily.
>
> Later, when we had a water cart given and two donkeys were pur-
> chased locally these did the job. However, if the pump was damaged
> through mishandling, or by small boys throwing pebbles into the tube,
> repairs were often not forthcoming for some time. In these circum-
> stances, on moonlit nights at about 2 a.m. the donkeys were inspanned
> and driven down into the sandy river-bed, where a deep hole was dug

in which, by and by, water gathered and was collected. This was repeated until there was enough water to fill the drum, after which the cart was pulled and pushed up the steep banks.

We could never allow a drop of water to be wasted. We had a few trees and shrubs and sometimes grew a few flowers and vegetables and they were all in constant need of the precious fluid.

When exceptionally heavy rainfalls caused tanks to overflow, everyone in the locality was invited to come and help himself.

The water concern was far from being the only one to be faced—our problems were legion—but despite them there remains in the heart gratitude to God for His help in the never-ending difficulties, and gratitude, too, for help and advice received from kind farmers and loyal comrades and friends from among the surrounding tribes.

Lieut.-Colonel Kirby, now Territorial Commander for Nigeria, describes the local situation as he first encountered it, and unfolds what happened:

Early in 1948, we were appointed to take charge of the work in the Semokwe District with our headquarters at Mbembeswana, where The Salvation Army had been carrying on medical work for a number of years. Senior-Captain Ruth Hacking was the nurse in charge of the dispensary. The Semokwe area is one of the driest parts of Rhodesia; very often the rainfall is only two or three inches each year and Mbembeswana is situated in a particularly dry spot, with the result that at times it was necessary to go four miles in each direction for every drop of water used at the dispensary. Furthermore, Mbembeswana is on the edge of the area in which we were working. Because of this, we decided that it would be much more satisfactory if the district headquarters could be transferred to a more central position in relation to the various corps in the area and also to a place where there was an adequate supply of fresh water.

After carrying out a survey, a request was made to Territorial Headquarters to move the district headquarters a distance of thirty miles, to a place called Tshelanyemba, where there was an adequate supply of water. When the move was made, my wife and I, with our one daughter, went down to Tshelanyemba, where we lived in the back of our vanette while we built a temporary house for ourselves on the site that had been chosen. As the work at Mbembeswana could not develop because of lack of water, it was decided to retain only a small maternity clinic at that place under the supervision of a local African nurse. Seeing that Senior-Captain Hacking was quite new to the country, and had therefore had very little experience in tropical nursing, permission was granted for her to go to the Bulawayo General Hospital for a few months in order to gain more experience.

At Tshelanyemba, we moved into our temporary dwelling; and as we started to supervise the work from this centre it soon became known that Mrs. Kirby was a nurse, with the result that people started coming to us for treatment. There were no medical facilities anywhere in that particular area, the nearest being some thirty miles away. More and more people came, and after we had been there just a few weeks it was not an uncommon sight for us to see twenty or even thirty people sitting outside our back door when we got up in the morning, all waiting for treatment. Very often some of these people were far too sick to be coming as out-patients, and it became obvious that if we were to meet the need it would be necessary for us to have some place where we could keep one or two in-patients. This matter was discussed with the local community and they agreed that they would come and make bricks so that we could erect a small four-roomed building, where we could have a dispensary and four beds to be used by patients requiring hospitalization.

As soon as the building was completed, we employed an African nurse to work under Mrs. Kirby's direction, as there was far too much for her to cope with alone. The work continued to grow so quickly that within a matter of a few weeks it was necessary for us to erect a second building, and this one was literally *built around beds on which patients were lying*. By the time the second building was completed the then Major Hacking had completed her period at the Government General Hospital and so returned to us at Tshelanyemba.

The work then steadily grew and every month more and more people were coming to us for treatment. People were walking forty, fifty and even sixty miles through the bush. Very often they would come in large parties and remain with us until all the patients were well again. Major Hacking did valiant service and became well known throughout the area. She was a hard worker, commencing early in the morning and often working through until after dark with hardly a break.

By 1950 it became apparent to us that a proper hospital was needed to meet the need of the people in the area. Territorial Headquarters were informed of the situation and one day, when the Territorial Commander visited us to see the work being done in the two buildings containing eight beds, he found over thirty in-patients occupying every available bit of space in these buildings: this, in addition to the hundreds of out-patients attending each day.

Following this visit, we drew up plans for a thirty-five-bed hospital, which was soon approved by the Government medical department. Plans were submitted to International Headquarters with a request for the sum of £3,000, which was the estimated cost of erecting this urgently needed hospital, but unfortunately the reply was that, due to heavy commitments for medical work in other countries, it was not possible for any funds to be made available for the extension of medical work in Rhodesia, and it would probably be some time before we could expect any grant toward the building of such a hospital. The Rhodesia Territory was not in a position to give any financial assistance; therefore it was regretted that the plans would have to be shelved for the time being.

This decision caused some of us at Tshelanyemba a great deal of concern, as we were seeing the great need every day and we felt that *something had to be done for the suffering people.* We made this a matter of prayer, asking the Lord to show to us His will. We prayed for quite a while before any indication as to what the Lord required. Then one day, when I was conducting a Sunday evening service for European miners on a nearby mine, I was speaking about the miracle of the loaves and fishes and brought out the point that Jesus did not just perform a miracle when the food was needed, but first of all told the disciples to see how much they had themselves, and it was when they introduced the fishes and the small loaves that Jesus took the little bit which they had and multiplied it. As I was speaking the Lord spoke to me and said: ' Do not continue to pray asking God to send money for the hospital; see what you can do yourselves first, and then God will take the little bit which you can do and multiply it.' As we thought about this, I told the Lord that I was prepared to undertake all the building, with the help of one or two labourers (as I had had some experience in this work) and my wife agreed to run the District while I was doing it, if the Lord would show us where the money for the materials was to come from.

A few days later, while reading the newspaper, I saw an advertisement, inserted by a fertilizer factory, asking for ' old bones ' for which they were prepared to pay £3 per ton. Due to the severe droughts in the area, which had resulted in many animals dying, there were large numbers of bones all around the countryside; and so word was passed around to the schools asking that these be collected by the schoolchildren and, a few weeks later, we had accumulated a heap of five tons of bones outside my office in Tshelanyemba. A neighbour loaned us a five-ton truck and they were loaded ready for the 100-mile trip to Bulawayo.

When we reached the factory, to my surprise I was told that, because of the desperate need, the price had risen to £9 per ton, and I came away with a cheque for £45! With this money we employed three labourers and commenced digging the foundations.

In the meantime, Territorial Headquarters had given permission for us to commence work on the hospital if we could raise funds. We therefore decided that we would try to put up perhaps one or two of the rooms on the main hospital block, and then extend it from time to time as money became available. However, with the £45 we employed the labourers, dug foundations, bought some cement and started work. Then a wonderful thing happened. Money started arriving in the post. It came from all over the world, much of it from people we had never heard of before, often with just a little note to say, ' The Lord has asked me to send this to you—. We do not know what your needs are but we are sure you can use it.' It soon became apparent that it was not the Lord's will that we just put up one or two rooms but that we go ahead with the whole scheme and, as the work proceeded, not once were we held up through lack of funds; and when the building was completed, a few months later, we actually had some cash in hand.

The building, now completed, required the furnishings; so a request was sent to the Beit Trustees asking if they would be interested in making a grant toward beds, blankets and other essential equipment. Within a few days a reply was received stating that they do not make grants for equipment, but that if we had some permanent scheme for water or electricity they might give a grant toward the cost of this. As their waiting list was so long, however, it could be two or three years before any funds were available.

As we considered this offer we remembered that the main power line, from Bulawayo, 100 miles away, to the mines in the area, passed within three-quarters of a mile of the hospital and when choosing the site we had had in mind the possibility of eventually bringing in the power: in fact when building the hospital we did in faith put in the electrical conduits and wired the building ready for the day when power would become available. Therefore we now asked the Beit Trustees for £1,200, to cover the cost of bringing the main power line into the hospital and for installing electric pumps to pump the water from the river into storage tanks, from which the hospital would be fed, thereby ensuring a regular supply to all wards.

Imagine our surprise when, two or three weeks later, we received word from the Beit Trustees to say that our request had been granted. They gave more than we had asked for; in fact, when we received the money there was not only sufficient for the electricity and the water but also some left over toward the cost of the equipment. On the 16th December, 1953, the hospital was opened by the Territorial Commander, Commissioner Theodore Holbrook, completely free of debt. Our original estimate for the project was £3,000 but the Lord sent to us a total of £5,000 in a little over a year! This enabled us not only to erect the hospital, have electricity and water, but also provided money for the erection of nurses' accommodation.

Brigadier Hacking continued to work at Tshelanyemba for a number of years, during which time hundreds of patients received treatment at this hospital. A magnificent work was carried on by the Brigadier and her assistants during the years which followed the opening.

An up-to-date picture of conditions at Tshelanyemba is provided by a recent report:[19]

To the staff of the Army's Tshelanyemba Hospital in the remote south-west corner of Rhodesia, this is home. Major Evelyn Munn, the matron, Major Doris Wight from Canada and Rhodesian-born Staff Nurse Theresa Hever, supervise and administer the forty-five (officially thirty-three) bed hospital and the African nursing staff.

The need for medical missionaries, further equipment and new buildings in this corner of Africa is great.

Disease is rife and yearly drought inevitably leaves in its wake hunger and malnutrition, problems the staff are effectively combating with modern drugs and gifts from ' Freedom from Hunger ' and ' Oxfam ', and also with prayer and simplicity of faith.

Quick and accurate diagnosis is not easy when dealing with a people who cling to their ancient superstitions. Illness, they claim, is the result of an evil spirit entering the body and is sent by an enemy, through the streak of lightning that scars the sky above their huts. This fear of sickness often obscures their judgment when describing the condition of a relative lying sick in a distant village.

' I often wonder how I will react in an emergency,' says Major Munn. ' But when emergencies come, as they often do, the right action is taken automatically, almost without thought. A little later, having had time to think, I wonder how I did it.' She smiles: 'And then I know that we are in God's hands.'

Chapter Five

TRAINING
PROGRAMMES

THE Church has a duty to support all that contributes to the welfare of man.

In co-operation between Church and Government many valuable forms of service present themselves. These lie particularly in the fields of health, nursing and para-medical training programmes and the extension of rural clinics and public health. ... The Christian concept of healing ... may sometimes necessitate the continuance of existing institutions or the development of new ones. ...

> From *The Healing Church*, The Tübingen Consultation, 1965. World Council Studies No. 3—World Council of Churches, Geneva, 1965.

ZAMBIA

The medical work of The Salvation Army in Zambia, formerly Northern Rhodesia, had its beginnings in 1927 at Ibwe Munyama, where a dispensary attached to the Salvation Army boarding school took care of the sick in the district. It was decided to continue the work on a more ambitious scale, however, and it was transferred in 1945 to Chikankata, on a fertile plateau forty miles from the railhead at Mazabuka and eighty miles from Lusaka, now the capital of the Republic of Zambia. At the time this meant the establishment of a thirty-five-bed hospital in bush country surrounded by numerous villages, many of the people having moved up to the plateau from the disease-ridden valley area. Others came later, in order to be within easy reach of the medical care provided by the hospital.

In June, 1945, although the hospital was not yet completed, Captain Janet Watson commenced dispensary work, which she continued to direct until the first Medical Superintendent, Senior-Captain (Dr.) K. E. Mortimer and Mrs. (Dr.) Mortimer arrived. Succeeding Medical Superintendents and Chief Medical Officers have included Colonel (Dr.) Wm. T. B. McAllister (1947–51), Brigadier (Dr.) Sidney Gauntlett (1951–67), Dr. Gordon Carter, a Baptist missionary from Canada who, with his wife, has given invaluable service in the absence of the resident Chief Medical

Officer from 1967–70, as well as in an earlier period, from 1955–56, and Captain (Dr.) Paul Duplessis (since 1970).

Chikankata nurse training programme

The hospital was officially opened in May 1947, by the then Governor of Northern Rhodesia, Sir John Waddington. In the same year a request was made by the Northern Rhodesian Government to The Salvation Army for nurses' training to be commenced. Prior to this, many mission hospitals had undertaken their own nurse training programmes, issuing a hospital certificate. The Government had for some years been training young men as Medical Assistants, but it was seen that the role of women in the field of nursing must be fulfilled, now that girls were receiving education.

Great difficulty was encountered in securing girls with sufficient education for the course, as few girls ever reached Standard 6, the end of primary school, which was considered the necessary educational qualification. Of the few who did, most married as soon as they completed their primary education, whilst others chose to train as teachers, which they felt was a more attractive way of life and far less demanding, while the course for teacher training lasted only two years. The difficulty is the more readily understood from the fact that statistics prove that in 1951 only seventeen girls in the whole of Northern Rhodesia reached Standard 6, though happily this number increased each year.

During the formative years, the nurse training programme at Chikankata was in the hands of a very capable Canadian Sister, Captain Edith Jater, later to become the Supervisor of nurses in the Grace Hospital, Calgary, Canada. A good foundation was laid, and the pattern followed by other training schools. The first class commenced with seven girls, though in a very short time the number was reduced to two, who successfully completed the course, passing their final Government Examination in November 1950.

The first type of training to be undertaken was a three-year course in general nursing, during which the candidates studied anatomy and physiology, medicine and surgery, and medical and surgical nursing. A hospital and government preliminary examination was taken at the end of the first year, and a final hospital and government examination at the end of the third year. Later on, a one-year post-graduate compulsory service was instituted, as it was felt that the nurses did not have enough experience to go

out and cope with the demands of a rural health centre. It was
soon realized that to have general training alone was not sufficient
and that midwifery training would have to be introduced.

In 1955 extensions to the hospital were opened, providing
130 beds, the increased room being made possible by the addition
of five new wards, and isolation block and other buildings,
including theatre block, kitchen and administration block and
X-ray department. The Beit Trust and the Northern Rhodesian
Government financed this project. Placing a modern hospital in
the midst of people unused to western medicine was a bold
experiment but one which justified itself.

Zambian nurse training requirements

In 1961 Independence arrived and the Zambia registered nurse
training, based on the syllabus of Great Britain, was commenced
at a government hospital; then two years later the Zambia enrolled nurse training was introduced. All training schools that
had been doing the three-year Medical Assistant Course were
notified that they must change over to the two-year training—a
two-year practical training. The syllabus to be covered included
teaching in basic anatomy and physiology, hygiene—especially in
relationship to village life in Zambia—preventive health measures, and medical and surgical nursing, the emphasis again
being made on diseases known in Zambia. The educational
standard set for this training is Form II (two years of secondary
schooling). This in actual fact is now no higher in academic
achievement than the Standard 6 earlier demanded. An average
intake of twenty student nurses twice a year gives approximately
sixty students being trained concurrently, the loss rate still being
fairly high.

All Christian hospitals felt that the nurses were both too young
and too inexperienced to work without supervision after so short
a training, and so permission was sought from the Government
to institute a one-year post-qualification training. This would
benefit both nurse and training school, as those schools which
had previously had a third-year training course and, like ourselves,
were never able to keep trained staff, because of the attractive
salaries offered by the copper mines and government hospitals,
were to find staff very sadly depleted.

The nurses who enrolled to train at Chikankata were asked to
sign that they would agree to stay for a further year of training;
during this year the students are given lectures in *materia medica*
and ward management, undertake theatre training and are taught

simple surgical procedures such as tooth extraction and suturing of simple wounds. More recently included in this additional year is child care, each nurse spending some time in the under-fives clinic.

Rural health

Visits are arranged to nearby villages, and some of the nurses have given simple lectures on child care and village hygiene with the help of posters and flannelgraph material. Some have visited home league (women's) meetings to talk with the mothers, whilst others have accompanied the doctors on their visits to the out-lying clinics to help in the vaccination programme.

In the early days of the hospital there were not more than eight students. This was considered the number needed to run the hospital efficiently but today (1970), with 240 beds, an average student body consists of twelve midwifery trainees, working only on the midwifery department—two groups of twelve doing their post-qualification year and approximately sixty student nurses. It is envisaged that we shall eventually increase the total to 100.

Approximately 450 applications were received for the one intake of nurses offering twenty places, which shows the great advance made in the past two decades in the field of education for girls.

Midwifery training

With the commencement of the Kariba hydro-electric scheme, better roads through the Zambezi Valley were built; improvements in standard of living followed because of the work and material gain this brought, but the need for trained people in all fields remained.

Midwifery training, mentioned earlier, is still available only to the privileged few; many applications are received from nurses who have done their training in other hospitals, but in the main student midwives are taken from our own general nurse trainees. A one-year course is given. No domiciliary midwifery being done in this area, the whole year is spent in the hospital. A hospital and government examination is set, and the successful candidates are enrolled as midwives.

Chikankata Hospital has taken a very active part in much of the ' spade work ' which has been done, since Zambia attained its Independence, in bringing the training programme into line with that in other countries. The Tutor has served on the Examinations Sub-committee of the Medical Council of Zambia and has helped in the revising of rules and syllabi for the Zambia enrolled nurse training, and the Matron has served on both the Examination and Nursing Committees. Both have acted as external examiners for the government examinations and from time to time matrons and tutors from other hospitals have visited Chikankata to gain information on the training. The shortened two-year training programme was instituted because of the great need for nurses, and in many ways is best suited to the type of girl offering herself, but it is obvious that, in spite of the fact that the Government has commenced state registered nurse training, the enrolled nurses will have to accept the responsibility of staffing the rural health centres, often miles from a larger hospital and with no means of contacting them.

Dispensing and laboratory assistant training

Another facet of the Chikankata training programme is the training of dispensing and laboratory assistants, undertaken jointly by the pharmacist, Captain (now Lieut.-Colonel) Thomas McKenzie, now in New Zealand, and the doctor—the doctor being responsible for the laboratory assistant training.

The first young man to be trained had completed his primary education at Chikankata school, obtaining a Standard 6 certificate. After securing a hospital certificate this young man soon left us to go to a government hospital, where he worked for many years.

In 1956 this training was officially established, and two young men were accepted for the course, one successfully completing it. There is now a three-year course in elementary laboratory technology which is recognized by the Medical Council of Zambia, combined with training in elementary dispensing and not officially recognized. Major Jean Fardon, herself a trained pharmacist, organized the course and was in charge of this training for ten years. This combined course was designed to meet the needs of smaller hospitals which could not afford the use of full-time laboratory technicians but which also needed a part-time dispenser. The education standard is Form II. A government examination in laboratory procedure is taken and government certificates issued at the end of the third year. The Chikankata laboratory supervisor has regularly served as an official examiner. By 1969, twenty-five male students had entered the course since its inception, ten having successfully passed the government examination, whilst ten were still in training.

Brief training of two to three months has also been given in very elementary laboratory procedures for personnel from small Christian hospitals. The need is felt for more highly qualified laboratory technicians for the larger hospitals in Zambia and this is to be met by a new course which is being offered by the Government. Equally important is the need for laboratory assistants to work in smaller hospitals and dispensaries. It is therefore envisaged that the type of training now given at Chikankata will be continued for some years to come.

We at Chikankata are glad of the opportunity to play a part in the development of this young country, a development which is forging ahead rapidly (writes Major Edith Shankster, Matron at the Chikankata Hospital, concluding the foregoing record). We feel that we must make the most of the time ahead of us in helping to train the indigenous youth to meet the challenge of their day.

CATHERINE BOOTH HOSPITAL, NAGERCOIL, INDIA

Nursing is a science, an art and a vocation, calling for a trinity of head, hand and heart. No nurse can be well prepared without attention to all of these. The Good Samaritan, the first male nurse, was touched in his heart; he used his hands skilfully and had some knowledge of what his patient needed. Dedicated hearts and hands are indispensable to nursing today, but how much greater is the demand on the head! Catherine Booth Hospital in Nagercoil, India, is equipped to provide this threefold preparation.

From the inception of the hospital, practical nursing was taught to young Indian Salvationists by Mrs. Colonel Turner, the nurse-wife of the Chief Medical Officer. In 1939 the ' Training School ' was recognized by the Madras Government through the Nurses' Auxiliary of the Christian Medical Association of India. The course conducted was ' lower grade ', and a pass in third form was a sufficient educational qualification for entry. In 1947 His Highness the Maharajah of Travancore opened the first School of Nursing building. The government also raised the status of the school from lower to ' higher grade '. Entrants must now have completed high school. From the commencement all teaching was done and examinations conducted in English. Both men and women students were admitted, enjoying equal status and opportunity.

Catherine Booth Hospital School of Nursing still functions under what is now designated the Examining Board of the Nurses' League of the Christian Medical Association of India, a body which has set high standards a little above government requirements. The board requires the active co-operation of the staff of all its member schools in such tasks as the setting and conduct of examinations and the preparation of standard text-books. Lieut.-Commissioner (Dr.) Harry Williams was for some years the President.

The main courses offered in the school of nursing are a three-year course in general nursing with obstetric and community nursing (public health) integrated and a nine-month midwifery course for graduate nurses. For some years the school also offered a six-month post-basic course in reconstructive surgical wards and operating theatres. This is temporarily in abeyance due to lack of a qualified plastic and orthopaedic surgeon. Also in abeyance is a post-basic course in ophthalmic nursing since the eye specialist, Major (Dr.) Alloway, became Chief Medical Officer. All entrants to the school are bonded to serve for a year as junior staff nurses on completion of the course. During this year, and for those who join the staff beyond it, there is a programme of inservice education under the leadership of Mrs. Major Alloway, B.Sc., R.N.

According to the prospectus of the school, candidates for selection must have passed the Secondary School Leaving Certificate at first attempt with sixty per cent marks. In fact, twenty-five per cent of the candidates selected (through exami-nation and interview) have had some college education. The curriculum, which includes physics, chemistry, psychology and sociology, fully meets the requirements of the Indian Nursing Council and compares favourably with that offered in good basic schools of nursing in other parts of the world. Because of the lowered standard of English required under the present school and college systems, English has to be taught with other subjects in the first year. It is likely to remain the medium of instruction for some years, at least in South India. Most of the candidates admitted are between seventeen and twenty-one years of age. They come from a cross-section of society and all branches of the Christian church as well as other religions. Most are given a small stipend from the school of nursing to cover board, and enough pocket money for the barest needs. They enjoy student status. All share the burden of work in the hospital wards and departments as well as the public health unit, but the work is part of the learning process. Careful planning ensures that each gets the recommended minimum of supervised experience in all departments at a time when it should be meaningful. Apart from the medical college hospital schools, probably no other school of nursing in South India has such a breadth of clinical experience to offer its students.

There are hundreds of applicants for the twenty-four seats offered annually in the school of nursing. Careful selection, including a selection examination and interview, means that student wastage is low. No one leaves for marriage, and few of their own volition. Most who enter are therefore with us for almost five years. Since the entrants are young (between seventeen and twenty-one years of age) and come from a cross-section of society, what an opportunity to influence their lives and a developing society through them!

After years of struggle with pitifully inadequate facilities the school of nursing now has well-equipped buildings adequate for present needs. The extent and functional usefulness of the present school of nursing complex is largely due to the vision and vigour of Lieut.-Commissioner (Dr.) Williams, who also, in building and altering wards, ensured that good nursing would be possible. He agreed with the Superintendent of Nurses that ' good nursing can be taught only where good nursing is practised '.

The school of nursing and nursing service at Catherine Booth Hospital are still the responsibility of one head—the Superintendent of Nurses. It is the present policy of the Examining Board to have these under two separate heads who would co-ordinate together and enjoy equal status. While this could present problems, it is patent that either load of responsibility is now more than enough for one pair of shoulders, however willing. The present Superintendent of Nurses, Major Sughanantham, is an Indian officer male nurse who, with his wife (the Out-patients' Sister) graduated from the first class. He has diplomas in genito-urinary nursing from London and in teaching and supervision from the Christian Medical College at Vellore, and assisted the last Superintendent of Nurses for eleven years. An American missionary officer with a B.Sc. in nursing is Director of Nursing Studies (Principal Tutor). There are four other Indian and non-Indian nurses on the staff with degrees in nursing, and two with diplomas in midwifery teaching. A young Indian officer-nurse who has already gained her diploma in public health and pioneered the hospital's public health programme is at present studying for her B.Sc. in nursing. Apart from the Superintendent of Nurses and the Director of Nursing Studies, all these are in charge of wards or departments in addition to their teaching responsibilities in the classrooms.

Catherine Booth Hospital School of Nursing does not conceal

its Christian aims. It accepts candidates from all branches of the
Christian church as well as non-Christians. They are not required
to become Christians or to join The Salvation Army in order to
enrol, and they are told that no pressure will be put on them after
enrolment. They are also told that it is a Christian school where
they will be subject to Christian influences. They will be expected
to attend morning prayers and Sunday worship and participate in
Bible study. Despite the mounting pressures against Christian
missionary work in India, there is still a wide open door for
introducing Christ to the student in a Christian school of nursing.
Coercion is out, but is it Christian anyway? Those who know
Christ can introduce Him as a friend.

Over four hundred nurses have passed through Catherine
Booth Hospital School of Nursing and gone out to work in all
parts of India, in the Arabian Gulf, in Aden, and even England,
Canada and U.S.A. Almost to a ' man ' they have remained active
in nursing despite marriage. Most have acquitted themselves well
and some have risen to positions of leadership. Judging from the
reports of those who encounter them, many are finding in nursing
a truly Christian vocation and are being used as missionaries in
the places of their appointment.

Since the leadership is now in the hands of an Indian officer-
nurse and there are capable senior Indian nurses in the school and
hospital, is there any further need for missionary nurses? The
answer is, yes! The Superintendent of Nurses needs a capable
deputy with a diploma or degree in administration and some
experience in this field. There is plenty of need for senior personnel, but these would need some special preparation in nursing
apart from the spiritual and other qualifications required of a
missionary. There is a happy international team of nurses at the
hospital, but working as a team requires much grace and humility
if harmony is to be preserved. In particular, no one should apply
unless she is prepared to work under an Indian nurse or, if needed
for a key position, to plan to prepare others for leadership and
make herself dispensable.

*Brigadier Vera Williamson, until recently the Superintendent of
Nurses at the Catherine Booth Hospital, who contributes the foregoing
record, has significant views on nursing education and writes:*

The expression ' nursing training ' has not been used with
reference to the present programme because I consider that the
nurse of today needs more than training alone. She needs an
education in nursing. Indeed, I believe that no educational

preparation can be too great, so long as it is really geared to nursing and the student has her heart in it.

Nursing and nursing education, I feel, should be left entirely to nurses.   This was Florence Nightingale's conviction, and nursing is not truly a profession where this has not been accomplished.

Captain Terence K. Willey, who is in charge of the School of Radiography at the Catherine Booth Hospital, writes:
In the middle nineteen-fifties, the Christian Medical Association of India set up a sub-committee to organize and conduct a training programme for diagnostic radiographers.   Two of the five mission hospitals accepted for this new project were the Thomas Emery Hospital, Anand, and the Catherine Booth Hospital, Nagercoil.   Captain Ken Tutton, M.S.R., was the Secretary of the newly formed committee, and he and Captain Frank Ockleston, M.S.R., were examiners selected to set and mark the intermediate and final papers in connection with the two-year diploma course.

The teaching in the school of radiography was under the direction of Captain Ockleston and Dr. N. Sitaram, B.Sc., M.B., B.S., M.R.C.P., who had had considerable experience in the field of radiology.   The standard set was high, being based on the syllabus and requirements of the London Society of Radiographers with additions and modifications necessitated by the peculiar needs of the mission hospitals in India.

When Captain Ockleston left India, his place was taken by Miss O. Sutton, M.S.R., M.N.Z.S.R., from New Zealand, and I followed Miss Sutton in 1967.   We still undertook the diploma course but, due to a need for radiographers with less extensive training, we commenced a shorter certificate course, maintaining the high standard but within a smaller scope.   Three or four students are taken each year from the large number of applicants and, after qualification, they find employment in mission hospital and private clinics, or they go on to further studies in the larger medical colleges.

PART FOUR

Tackling Needs in Many Lands

Chapter
One

TUBERCULOSIS

' THE Christian can never isolate one aspect of his work and take it as a gift to a new country or people. He has to involve himself in the situation as he finds it, and identify himself with the needs and problems of the people who become his people, and share with them the love of his God until they accept Him as Father. . . .

' To plan new campaigns from armchairs at home will lead only to new problems. The strength of the Church is its compassion, and the effectiveness of its mission lies in the dedication of its members not to a cause but to people.'

Daniel A. Andersen and Paul W. Brand
in *Ethical Responsibility in Medicine*
(E. S. Livingstone Ltd., London and
Edinburgh, 1967)

INDIA

When Colonel (Dr.) Daniel Andersen was Chief Medical Officer at the Evangeline Booth Hospital, Ahmednagar, India, he wrote for American readers in 1958, of the work immediately behind him and reported: ' In point of age this hospital is the " baby " of the major Salvation Army hospitals in India, being just over eighteen years old. During this time the *Dagadi Davakhana* (stone hospital) has become known throughout the district of Ahmednagar of 1,400,000 people, and probably there is no village from which one or more patients have not come.

' In these eighteen years we have been able to initiate nurses' training in the district and also to provide the very first special beds for the treatment of tuberculosis. We have also co-operated in founding the Anti-Tuberculosis Association, so placing attacks against tuberculosis on a wider basis. This association carried out BCG vaccination in the city of Ahmednagar before the Government took up the problem generally.

' We have had the opportunity of studying the special diseases to which villagers are prone and have contributed some reports about these to scientific journals. We are now engaged in a nutrition study under the auspices of the Indian Council of Medical Research, New Delhi.'

Village Health Programme, 1970

A recent report (1970) of the Village Health Programme being operated from the Evangeline Booth Hospital, Ahmednagar, contains the following information and significant observations. It is by Captain (Dr.) Melvin Brieseman, M.B., Ch.B (New Zealand), the present Chief Medical Officer:

'Ahmednagar is in the centre of Maharashtra, 75 miles north-west of Poona on the Decca Plateau. The population of the township is 116,000 and of the district one and three quarter million. The area is mainly a farming district, but much of the soil is poor and rocky and most of the monsoon rain is shed on the slopes of the plateau nearer the coast. This means the rainfall is scant, with frequent droughts causing crop failure.

' The result of this is a poor economy, with fifty per cent of the population earning an average Rs. 21–55 per head per year ($3–8) and twenty-two per cent an income of less than Rs. 21 ($3) per head per year.

' In this situation the American Marathi Mission founded a hospital in 1904, for women and children. In 1939 the hospital was taken over by The Salvation Army, and thereafter utilized as a general hospital and extended to 166 beds, of which at present sixty are T.B., fourteen are for orphan children, ten general paediatric, seven maternity, eighteen private and the remaining general, medical and surgical beds.

' The service is available to all who come, but there are many in the villages around who are unable to come to hospital because of pressure of work in the fields or lack of money.

' The commonest diseases seen in the hospital are tuberculosis, gastro-enteritis and typhoid fever with malnutrition, tetanus, diphtheria and whooping cough high on the list. It can be seen that these diseases are preventable. But those who have no time or money for the treatment of established diseases cannot be expected to take action in the prevention of disease.

' Yet even greater than the need for prevention of these diseases is the need to deal with the basic problem of the society, that of over-population. The whole country is overcrowded. There are insufficient schools and colleges; qualified people such as engineers cannot find work; a large percentage of the population is underfed and, in spite of the Government's best effort at increasing food production, the population continues to increase at a greater rate. Diseases of poverty and tuberculosis are already too common. The only way to deal with all these problems is to deal with the population explosion, and yet one cannot limit a family without a guarantee that the existing family is protected in as many ways as possible.

' Because of this, the Evangeline Booth Hospital would like to extend its present work into the more needy areas around. Government and private efforts are made, but they are still insufficient. In one area surveyed, less than a mile from the hospital, fifty per cent of the people needed family planning advice, only twelve per cent of the children had triple vaccine and no polio vaccine, and no tetanus toxoid. In addition, the usual water and sanitation problems were present. In villages, there are nearer eighty per cent families needing planning advice, and no triple vaccine or polio has been given.

' So many of the medical troubles as well as educational, social and economic difficulties are due to over-population. For this reason, the hospital is expanding its work in the field of public health, family planning and village health work. Medical teams are at present visiting twelve villages around Ahmednagar and slum areas within the city. As there are eighty-four villages within twenty miles of the township and in the district, the work performed is capable of more extension.

' The staff at present available is working to full capacity and cannot extend, but if finance is available, further teams could be added, then more could be done.'

*   *   *

' The Christian surgeon . . . must not be a mere surgical scientist and technician. Even the simplest operation must not be to him just a mechanical business akin to the artisan's craft. His therapy ought to exemplify all those immeasurables that constitute good patient care.

' Lip service is given to the treatment of " the whole man ", to the treatment of people rather than diseases, but the principle is rarely well practised. . . . Who, than the Christian surgeon, should be better fitted to guide the real implementation of the treatment of the whole man? '

Evan Thompson, Surgeon,
Princess Alexandra Hospital,
Brisbane, Australia.

in *The Christian Physician in the Advance of the Science and Practice of Medicine*

(2nd International Congress of Christian Physicians, Oxford, 11–15 July, 1966).

JAPAN

Writing on the healing of ' the whole man ', Major Taro Nagasaki, M.D., F.A.C.C.P., Chief Medical Officer of the Booth Memorial Hospital, Tokyo, has declared: ' It is a challenge and honour for us to serve the whole man, created by God in His own image, and existing on the physical, mental and spiritual level. We serve the whole man not by our own choice but because it is God's will that we should do so, and because He has shown us His goodness. Sure of His guidance, we count our service no sacrifice; but simply a consequence of hearing and obeying God, our heavenly Father.'

Major (Dr.) Nagasaki was among those who deeply rejoiced in the opening in Suginami-Ku, Tokyo, of the three-storied Booth Memorial Hospital, dedicated to the glory of God and the whole healing of the suffering on November 23, 1968, the fifty-third anniversary of the foundation of the earlier Suginami Sanatorium. The event took place in the presence of Her Imperial Highness, Princess Chichibu of Japan, and Lieut.-Commissioner Wm. J. Parkins, then The Salvation Army's Territorial Commander for the U.S.A. Western Territory.

It was a fitting moment, Major Nagasaki felt, to recall the devoted service of Mrs. Colonel Yamamuro, pioneer of Salvationist interest in women's welfare in Japan, and of Dr. Sanya Matsuda, O.F., and Lieut.-Colonel Rin Iwasa, O.F., who dedicated their lives to the Army's medical work in Japan in earlier-days. ' The completion of the new building we owed to the committed leadership of Commissioner Koshi Hasegawa, former Territorial Commander, and his territorial staff,' the Chief Medical Officer has written. ' He has often inspired us with the slogan, " Hats off to the past! coats off to the future ".'[20]

Writing of the past, Major Nagasaki referred to The Salvation Army's medical work in the country having been for long regarded as of a charitable nature, with the tendency, now that social security was developing, to think that the need for it was becoming less. An effort therefore had to be made to show that a service with Christian motivation to all classes was indispensable. He continued:[20]

' Since the advent of anti-T.B. chemotherapy and surgical tuberculosis treatment, our sanitorium has been obliged to change its designation to that of a chest hospital, able not only to isolate declared tuberculosis patients but also to perform the indicated treatments.

'The change was mainly planned by Lieut.-Colonel (Dr.) Clifford Seamans, M.D.,* of the U.S.A., who earlier served in Japan, and has been continued successfully with the planning of the new building. Medical staff and nurses working in the Suginami Sanatorium were prepared to undertake non-tuberculosis medical and surgical care of patients with other forms of chest disease and, because of the declining need of tuberculosis beds in our community, we were quite willing to engage in the new field of chest (and related) diseases. For this reason internal and extra-mural training of our staff was encouraged, so that all might be better qualified for the new work.

'It was becoming unnecessary to run two Salvation Army sanatoria here in Japan, and after careful discussion among the administrative staff at both centres it was recommended to Territorial Headquarters that Suginami Sanatorium should function as a hospital for chest diseases and eventually Kiyose (Sei Shin) Sanatorium become a geriatric hospital. The united planning for both centres that took place at Territorial Headquarters followed a concept of area-wide planning. What was needed was an over-all or master plan, combining not only measures to meet present needs but also those which would be arising in the following twenty or thirty years. This type of planning was made possible by employing the knowledge of hospital administration granted me in Columbia University, through a scholarship provided by the U.S.A. Eastern Territory.

'Following the dedication of the new building, the former name, Suginami Sanatorium, was exchanged for that of *Booth Memorial Hospital*, the present premises accommodating out-patient department, administrative department, kitchen, X-ray department, laboratory, two operating theatres, central supply department and fifty-four non-tuberculosis beds.

'Shortly after the dedication, we started to plan the realization of the second stage in our master plan. This was to renovate the obsolete tuberculosis wards, in the Kiyose Sanatorium most in need of reconstruction. In order to start the second stage in the plan we needed to be satisfied that the functioning of the new building was good for the over-all administration of our hospital, and meeting the rapid increase in the running cost of the whole hospital.

'We are trying to excel, among local doctors, in our medical speciality of chest diseases such as cardiac diseases, bronchial

* See p. 78.

asthma, emphysema, chronic bronchitis, pulmonary cancer, and so on, in order that we may be a witness for our Lord through the medical competence and Christian nature of our service.

'It is most important, for the healing ministry of a Christian hospital, to organize a co-operatively united healing team, which consists of doctors of every speciality, nurses, dieticians, medical social workers, X-ray and laboratory technicians, a chaplain and so on. It is becoming commoner that group ministry is regarded as the more acceptable approach in hospitals. This is not to disparage individual witness, but to encourage Christian medical workers to commit themselves in integrated dynamic group approach in order to serve and heal " the whole man " who is suffering.'

Writing of future prospects, Major Nagasaki points out: ' Without the devoted service of Christian nurses it will be impossible to prove a good Christian hospital. Therefore it becomes the more urgent to start to establish a nurses' training school, which can be expected to supply us with good, well-qualified nurses, who are motivated by their Christian faith. . . . We should pray for the realization of such a nurses' training programme.'

One difficulty in recruiting voluntary workers locally for the hospital appears to be in the terms in which the people see their own social structure. ' It seems to me ', writes the C.M.O., ' that our people see the unit of community as the family, whereas western peoples see the individual as the unit. The individual-centred community is more interested in persons helping each other if each individual is fully mature. The family-centred community tends to help its own lineage only. Hence our hospital has difficulty in recruiting volunteer workers from our own community. Nevertheless, we are endeavouring to find them among Christian people. Our group of voluntary workers is gradually expanding and will prove that the community can serve the hospital, just as the hospital serves the community.'[20]

Chapter
Two

LEPROSY

' LEPROSY, as we know it, is one of the most ancient diseases to plague mankind and has afflicted most of the countries of the world at some time. . . . Through the centuries the word has several times changed meaning. Many biblical references to leprosy should probably be interpreted " defiled " or " cursed ", while the Hebrew word *saraath*, translated " leprosy " in the Authorized Version of the Bible covers a multitude of skin conditions.'[21]

' Whatever its meaning in past ages,' Brigadier (Dr.) Sidney Gauntlett has written, ' there is, in the light of present knowledge, no justification for a highly emotional reaction to leprosy, leading on the one hand to social segregation and the idea of being " unclean ", nor, on the other hand, an exaggerated sentiment expressed toward those afflicted.

' The stigma attached to leprosy has unhappily remained until recent times and even now persists in many parts of the world, an attitude born of ignorance. We now know that leprosy is not a curse; it is a disease caused, as many other illnesses affecting mankind, by a germ, infectious, but much less so than tuberculosis—and curable.'[21]

With leprosy thus ' put in its place ' among the other diseases that afflict mankind, what is the situation?

' Left untreated, the disease can cause almost unparalleled suffering and mutilation,' Dr. Gauntlett continues. ' Such neglect now is unnecessary and should occur less frequently as effective treatment becomes known and available to all. The infectiousness of the disease has certainly been exaggerated, but the limited knowledge we have even today of how the disease is spread does not warrant a casual approach.

' The discovery of sulphone drugs—chemically related to the sulphonamides—and their effective use in leprosy, revolutionized the treatment and management of this baffling and dangerous disease. Dapsome (diamino-diphenyl-sulphone), today's main drug, was used first in 1947 to treat leprosy, becoming more widely available later. . . . In more recent years other drugs have come into use, many of which are also most effective in treatment and valuable for those patients who cannot tolerate dapsome. Research continues at ever-increasing pace.'[21]

As Dr. Gauntlett further points out: ' In most countries hopeful signs are in evidence of the breakdown of ignorance and prejudice which has hindered leprosy treatment in the past and, in some areas, marked success in the war against this widespread, distressing, now curable disease. The patient and devoted service of many workers through the centuries, often with little encouragement from visible results, prepared the way for the heartening progress made during the last two decades in the battle against leprosy—far surpassing achievements of the previous thirty centuries.

'In no other field of medical science have Christian doctors been so obviously to the fore. The fight has been as much against deep-rooted fear and prejudice as against a bacillus and a disease: and perfect love casts out fear. We thank God that for the past sixty years Salvationists have been privileged to play a part in caring for these sick people and bringing enlightenment to all.

'For so long, little could be done for leprosy sufferers except practical demonstration of God's love. Deep caring, and readiness to share, eased suffering. This brought many to accept Jesus Christ and His offer of eternal life, the sufferer's supreme hope.'[21]

The latter paragraph describes the situation when, in 1909, the first Salvation Army colony for leprosy sufferers came into being. In the Prouw Valley of Central Java, in what were then known as the Dutch East Indies, hot springs had encouraged hopes of healing for the disease and a hospital had been erected, by private initiative. The hopes of the sufferers had faded but the patients, who had come from far afield, could not be dispersed. After a time the Government took charge of the situation and 'military were ordered to Pelantoengan to look after the patients —most of them practically incurable. . . . But the arrangement did not work too well '.[22]

It is now history that General van Heutsz—the Dutch Governor-General in 1909, and an eminent administrator—had shortly before, during a brief leave in the Netherlands, 'stayed in the house of friends who spoke in the highest terms of their Salvationist maid. It now occurred to him that possibly The Salvation Army might deal with the problem of the sufferers in the Government's care at Pelantoengan, the Government shouldering financial responsibility for the work '.[22]

His suggestion was accepted by The Salvation Army and, not surprisingly, conditions for the patients there were soon vastly improved. A Netherlands writer reported:

'A formidable change took place in the . . . running of the colony. It was machinery no longer; it became a " living work ". The driving force of those who now dealt with the patients was different from that of the soldiers.'[22]

Within a decade, five colonies had been established in the Indonesian islands and Salvation Army officers not only from the Netherlands but from America, Australia, Canada, China, Finland, France, Germany, Great Britain, Hungary, New Zealand, Sweden and Switzerland, as well as Eurasians and Javanese, became ministrants to the sufferers. Lieut.-Colonel Thomas Bridson, who with his wife spent many years in this ministry, wrote: ' It was a privilege to work with such noble souls of many nationalities.'

Problems of those days included depressive reactions on the part of patients whose hopes of a ' cure ' rose and fell, and even mental imbalance on the part of some. Incidents of danger to life and limb were not uncommon. ' Such incidents are liable to occur among people who endure so much suffering and have to spend their whole life in isolation with fellow-sufferers,' Lieut.-Colonel Bridson explained. ' But as a rule they live peaceably and happily together. Life . . . goes on remarkably smoothly, considering the number and various types of people, most of whom have no hope of recovery or of ever returning to normal life.'

The children of leprosy sufferers, were cared for outside the ' infected area ' until they could be placed with suitable families. Prospective foster-parents were required to visit the patents of an expected child and ask their consent to the adoption of their child.

Infected children—some brought with them by a parent on the latter's admission to the colony—were cared for by the officers. Government doctors were responsible to the health authorities for the medical oversight of all patients but it was the Salvation Army officers who, with the help of indigenous employees, carried out the actual treatments of patients.

Modern medical knowledge of Hansen's disease—as it came to be called, after Dr. Gerhard Armauer Hansen, a Norwegian, who in 1873 first expressed the view that it was caused by a bacillus (germ)—has altered the present picture out of all knowledge, but when The Salvation Army moved into Pelantoengan, chaulmoogra oil, taken by mouth or by injection, was the mainstay of leprosy treatment and had been since its discovery several centuries before Christ, although medical workers were constantly seeking new and more effective remedies. ' Salvation Army colonies saw some of the original research which, though not providing the remedy sought for, should not be overlooked.'[21]

' National officers served faithfully in the colonies, bringing the gospel of love and forgiveness to people who had little to hope for in this world. . . . Meetings were always so bright and happy, enlivened by hearty singing and inspiring testimonies that non-Christians could hardly fail to be impressed by the joys brought through Christian faith.'[21] Some were converted, and at their own request enrolled as Salvation Army soldiers.

Apart from some efforts toward alleviation of the lot of
leprosy sufferers in the West Indies—a home was opened in
Jamaica in 1917—Salvationist service to such patients had been
limited to the East Indies until 1928, when The Salvation Army
was asked to take over a home at Bapatla, founded in 1903 by
J. A. Christian, an Indian doctor in the Madras Provincial Medical
Service, and run for a number of years by the Baptist Mission.
Thus The Salvation Army took on its first leprosy hospital in
India, accommodating eighty patients. This was largely through
the faith and persistence of Commissioner Muthiah, a national
officer in charge of the work in that territory, who knew the offer
to be both a challenge and an opportunity. (The undertaking
ante-dated, by about three years, the dedication of a colony caring
for leprosy sufferers in Cochin, India.)*

The first Salvationist superintendent of the Bapatla centre,
which later became known as the Evangeline Booth Leprosy
Hospital, was Major Senaputra. Colonel (Dr.) Percy Turner
wrote, in his time, of the young Hindu student, belonging to the
Telugu Naidu Caste, who was attracted by the earnestness and the
message of The Salvation Army, eventually becoming an officer.
Renamed Senaputra—' Son of the Army '—this devoted Indian
began a life-work among the Tamil coolies and then the depressed
classes of his own race. After serving in educational and administrative work, he was given charge of the Bapatla Colony ' to
which he gave his best effort and care, his only sorrow being that
he could not do all he longed to do for the inmates. He ended as
he began, amongst the poorest and most needy; for finally his
health gave way and he died in Madras . . . giving a last testimony
of God's goodness and that all was well. But the work at the
colony continues '.

It is dedication such as his that has enabled Salvationists to
maintain the work among these needy people to the present day.
In modern times the Bapatla Leprosarium is a centre running
roadside clinics, in addition to providing care for those whose
disease, though arrested, has taken such toll that they continue to
need institutionalized care. The average length of stay in the
leprosy settlement has been markedly reduced, however, to less
than twelve months by the provision of the ' outside ' treatment
facilities.

Lieut.-Commissioner (Dr.) Williams, formerly the Chief
Medical Officer at the Catherine Booth Hospital, Nagercoil, pays
tribute to the work of Professor Paul Brand and others who have

* See p. 42.

opened new fields, making possible reconstructive surgery for leprosy sufferers following the new era of hope that has dawned. He writes of Brand's work:

' Trained in an orthopaedic discipline, he was appointed to the rapidly expanding Christian Medical College Hospital at Vellore, in Southern India, in the amorphous department of surgery. He not only laid the foundations of service in bone and joint surgery, but he brought an incisive mind and disciplined eyes to study those deformed hands and shuffling, bandaged feet of leprosy. His work was not only humanitarian and effective; it satisfied the high criteria of surgical science. Paul was made a Hunterian Professor at the Royal College of Surgeons in London, and his Hunterian oration was a new chapter for leprosy cripples.'[14]

Reticent about his own contribution to the field of reconstructive surgery, Dr. Williams writes about the plastic surgical problem that had to be faced in the case of some patients: ' Techniques employed by the pioneer plastic surgeons on the burned faces of R.A.F. pilots were applied to this new problem, and faces disfigured by leprosy were treated with success.

' In 1961 this field was opened up in Nagercoil, with the advantage of earlier experience and the published results of many others involved in the rehabilitation of leprosy victims.'[14]

A recent yearly report from Nagercoil—where fifteen per cent of the twenty-one trainees under the rehabilitation programme were former leprosy patients—indicates some measure of the progress made, in the following terms:

' October 1, 1968, the beginning of the financial year for the hospital, saw the setting up of a separate accounting system for the Rehabilitation Department, which includes the Vocational Training Centre. At the time the new training centre (for handicapped women) at Aramboly, where a branch hospital is situated, was still without an industrial electrical supply. Necessary switchgear and other machinery were beginning to arrive. The weaving section was functioning quite happily.

' Soon Mr. A. Sankaran, an ex-leprosy patient returned as blacksmith instructor from his training at Swedish Red Cross at Katpadi. Half-way through November the oxygen-acetylene equipment and cylinders of oxygen and acetylene arrived. . . . The official opening was scheduled for December 5, when our International Leader was visiting Nagercoil. After much persuasion the industrial electricity supply was turned on, less than forty-eight hours before the opening. Business had commenced! '

The local spinning mills provided the first customers for the trainees in metal work but, later, orders were secured from further afield, and satisfaction came not only with the money raised, but from the work now supplied for the eager people being helped under the vocational training programmes.

Extension to workshops is accompanied by preparation for future agricultural work ' which may overshadow our present training schemes in the future, as our area is predominantly agricultural—the well has been deepened, and storage tanks have been built in various parts of the grounds. . . . Coconut, banana, mango and lime trees have been planted '. A poultry rearing scheme has also been envisaged.

There are training departments in operation for handloom weaving, tailoring and watchmaking, in addition to the machine fabrication shops.   Captain George Scott, B.Sc. (Eng.), A.M.I.E.E., Dip.Ed., is the Rehabilitation Officer in over-all charge of the programme. Mr. Sundar Egbert, Technical Supervisor, is a Swiss-trained watchmaker with a varied background and experience. The fact that he is himself crippled by polio and confined to a wheelchair ' evokes a marked awareness of the potentialities of the project '.

As well as seeking to assist their own programme—through the raising of money by the production of hospital furniture, handloom articles, tailoring items, metal work and clock repairs— the Catherine Booth Hospital authorities look to the benevolence of others to assist them in their work for the less fortunate of their brethren. Though certain committees and missions are generous in their help, individual giving is a most valuable and appreciated means of support to the efforts being made.

The story of the development of leprosy care at Chikankata, Zambia (now the Army's largest leprosy centre), is a saga in itself. In 1949 an African national officer finding himself affected by the disease—a situation he at first tried to keep secret— eventually made his way with difficulty over mountain paths to Chikankata, where he knew The Salvation Army had a hospital. Here an officer-doctor from Scotland (Colonel Wm. McAllister) offered all that was then available—understanding care and chaulmoogra oil. Shortly after, sulphone drugs became available, bringing hope and a new approach to the treatment of leprosy. The doctor was able to treat the first patient with the new drug, and a small settlement for leprosy sufferers had been set up at a site across a stream from the hospital.

Within a few years, 450 patients were living at the Chikankata

Leprosy Settlement, which receives patients from all over the province, an area of 33,000 square miles. An outpost corps to the hospital was established, with the first patient as Envoy-in-Charge; and many fellow patients have sought salvation there and become soldiers of The Salvation Army.

Most significant, during recent years, in the treatment of leprosy has been the change of emphasis from institutional to home care, so that it is with some satisfaction that Brigadier (Dr.) Sidney Gauntlett, who had charge of the leprosy settlement during the greater part of its growth and development, has been able to record that 'at Chikankata the number of in-patients has dropped from 450 to 250, in about two years, by a system of out-patient supervision working through all the government and mission hospitals and clinics in the province, some fifty-five in all, scattered over a very large area'.

A significant paper, ' Leprosy Control in the Southern Province of Zambia ',[23] written by Dr. Gauntlett, who was responsible for leprosy treatment throughout the area, tells of the co-ordinated treatment programme for leprosy undertaken in the province, and its results in terms of control of the disease assessed in the area. This shows that, four years after the inception of the plan, there was ' a steady decline in the six-monthly and annual notifications of new cases of leprosy '; the average length of history had been ' reduced from 41.5 months in 1951 to 14 months in 1967; the incidence of deformity . . . in patients admitted to the Chikankata Leprosarium fell sharply before the inception of the provincial control programme when leprosy treatment first began at Chikankata ' and that ' thereafter there was a slight but fairly steady decline '.

' Partly on account of the steady reduction in incidence of leprosy in the province and presentation for treatment of the disease at an earlier stage, the number of in-patients has been markedly reduced.'[23]

As well as a corps, a school was added to the settlement at Chikankata and a home league for the women has been a regular feature of activity and teaching, while building operations have helped the patients to move with the times from ' pole and dagga ' type houses to Kimberley brick houses with thatched roofs, and buildings for school dispensary and meeting hall in permanent built brick.

Major Edith Shankster, Matron of Chikankata Hospital, and formerly sister-in-charge of the leprosy work (from 1958–63) has seen these developments with gratification and, from where she serves, continues to watch with the joy the progress of the work she so grew to love.

'Although the healing of the body is most important, we try to keep uppermost the fact that we are here to be used in the healing of the soul,' says a report from Chikankata. ' The ultimate objective of our work is to live out and to preach the gospel of Christ's salvation for all men.'

*   *   *

In all the work undertaken on behalf of leprosy sufferers, The Salvation Army has been grateful for the support of organizations and Christian friends throughout the world, including the British Leprosy Relief Association (LEPRA), the Leprosy Mission of Britain and New Zealand, Oxfam, the Emmaus Suisse Society (Switzerland), the Algemeen Diaconal Bureau (the Netherlands), and Help the Aged (U.K.).

Chapter
Three
FRESH HOPE FOR THE HANDICAPPED

WEST INDIES
A strange beginning
How many men and women have been fired to enthusiasm to do some great work for God and His children by the quiet inspiration of some lesser known person! This could be said to be the case in the commencement of work amongst the blind in the West Indies.

Official records declare that ' Major and Mrs. John Barrell commenced work amongst the blind in Jamaica, 1926 ', but Colonel Barrell would later have been the first to say that the inspiration for this work was a young woman—his own sister, Emma—who never left the shores of England; indeed she rarely travelled further than her own street, yet through her faith and Christian living Emma Barrell became the source of the inspiration that brought hope to hundreds of blind men, women and children.

Emma was a perfectly normal child, with intelligence above the average, but as the result of a serious illness at seven years of age she became deaf. Within a few years her powers of speech had failed. Although unable to communicate with others by normal means, she still enjoyed reading and writing, and one of her delights was the constant notes she exchanged with brother John. A few years later it became apparent that Emma was gradually losing her sight and would be totally blind.

Surely John and his wife were to be excused if they wept through their night of doubt and depression as they thought of Emma, and John's invalid mother now confined to bed. 'Why, why?' wondered John. 'And what of the future?' But night does not last for ever and, with the morning of faith renewed, came hope and a practical idea. John would encourage Emma to learn to read and write braille and learn the sign language for the blind. He and his wife, active Salvation Army officers, would also learn braille and sign language. In a few months' time communication between brother and sister became frequent again—until a letter from the Salvation Army headquarters arrived with its startling announcement that Major and Mrs. John Barrell were ' appointed to Jamaica, West Indies '.

Making a visit to his mother and sister, John decided to tell Emma the news first, before breaking it to his mother, now eighty years old. Emma waited patiently as her brother spelled out the message on the palm of her hand. She gasped as its implications dawned on her. Now John was spelling out— ' What about mother and you? What are we to do? What shall we say to Headquarters?' There was a moment's silence as Emma thought of her mother lying upstairs in bed, and she herself unable to help either of them. Tears started; then bravely, and with determination strengthened by faith, she spelled out on her brother's hand the words, ' He that loveth father or mother, brother or sister, more than Me is not worthy of Me.'

' This is our cup, and we must drink. . . . God will take care of us.'

With this promise ringing in their hearts, Major and Mrs. Barrell packed their possessions and prepared to travel to the West Indies. They arrived in Jamaica in 1926 and John Barrell was appointed as Divisional Commander for the Jamaica Division.

Soon after their arrival, Colonel Thomas Cloud, Territorial Commander for the West Indies Territory, as it was then called, invited Major Barrell to attend with him a local council meeting, the subject of which was ' The Welfare of the Teenager '. During the meeting the problem of blind young people was brought up for discussion, and there was genuine concern over the matter of at least 1,719 *known* blind persons, but the subject was quickly dropped when someone remarked that fifteen years previously the Government had taken up the matter and found that it would cost the country £15,000 a year—a sum which could not be provided.

There were no funds for any such purposes. Regretfully the meeting passed its decision: nothing could be done—there simply wasn't the money!

After the meeting, Colonel Cloud asked Major Barrell what he knew about blind people and learned of the letters in braille that passed between brother and sister. 'Could you teach braille?' the Colonel asked, and Major Barrell replied, 'What! with 50 corps and 100 societies to lead? Impossible! Perhaps Mrs. Barrell could.' Suddenly it dawned upon him that there had, after all, been a purpose in their having learned braille years ago. They could now teach it to others in Jamaica!

That week a notice appeared in *The Daily Gleaner*, a local newspaper, announcing that The Salvation Army was going to teach blind people to read and write, and inviting any blind person who wished to learn braille to contact the Salvation Army headquarters.

The first pupil was a man of fifty. A few days later he was joined by a girl of sixteen years of age whose Methodist mother had written immediately for her daughter, born blind. Soon there were thirty students, the youngest being nine and the eldest sixty-six.

To make a start with the work, money was needed for materials; and Major Barrell set himself the task of finding fifty friends, each to give him £2 for the project. One friend said, ' Sir, if you teach one blind person to read and write it will be worth £100! ' In a few days the money was secured, though when Major Barrell announced to a congregation of West Indians, and others, in a united holiness meeting that blind people were going to be taught to read and write, the meeting went into an uproar of laughter, quite a number of people rolling on the floor!

News of the venture reached England. General Bramwell Booth donated £50 toward the work, and friends in England sent seventy braille books. But it was obvious that, if the work was to continue, additional funds were needed. It was decided to ask for public support. A meeting was held in the Ward Theatre, attended by Government, Civic and Church leaders, as well as many Jamaicans from all walks of life.

The hushed crowd listened in silence as a retired schoolmaster was led forward and, spreading out his braille book and finding the place, announced, ' Our lesson for this service is taken from

Isaiah 42: 16.' Then he commenced to read, 'And I will bring the blind by a way that they knew not.' With fully a thousand people present, the quietness could be felt.

Could anyone in that vast audience, however, have been expected to grasp the full significance of those words? Could anyone have visualized, on that occasion, the work and facilities for blind persons that would develop in the years ahead, when an efficiently run school, with over 100 pupils, many of them attaining high scholastic achievement, would prove a far cry from the first crowded classroom?

Or could anyone have foreseen the workshops—now housed as a separate institution—providing employment for thirty or so persons, the blind machinists now so skilled that they are able to use industrial machines and manufacture over 2,000 garments of a high standard for Government hospitals?

From the time of the Ward Theatre meeting onward the work was established, and on October 28, 1928, a school was opened. The first two children to benefit were Álbertha, a shy little girl of twelve, and Clarence, a Chinese boy, who was a little older. Classes were held in the Divisional Headquarters and soon other children came along, until some seven or eight were enrolled. School was held in the mornings while the afternoons were devoted to teaching the older girls needlework and the boys chair-caning and mat-making. Conditions were extremely primitive, but it was a beginning.

The next step forward came when Colonel Mary Booth was Territorial Commander and a large house in Church Street, Kingston, was rented. It was a two-storey building and was duly named the Florence Booth Home for the Blind.

In 1937, from funds raised by private subscriptions, the original institute buildings were erected on the present site at 19½ Slipe Pen Road. There was then accommodation for thirty resident students and the premises stood in about half an acre of land. However, it was not long before the institute was over-crowded and extensions were being considered. An adjoining acre of land was purchased, and on this one and a half acres the present school stands.

The Government of Jamaica allocated from the Colonial Development Scheme the necessary money for extensions and improvements, so that on November 24, 1950, two new wings were opened, eventually making it possible to accommodate seventy-two residents. Though in 1958 extensive alterations to the premises were carried out, capacity accommodation was

reached several years ago and present facilities are totally inadequate.

Resident adults, plus eleven who attended daily, were earlier
employed in the industry department. Gradually the numbers
were increased and in 1955 the industry department was separated
from the school and workshops for the blind were opened at
1 South Avenue, Kingston Gardens.

Until 1957, the original establishment at Slipe Pen Road was
accepted as an institution, but not recognized as a place of
learning. It was necessary to prove its status, and that year, for
the first time, four children were entered as candidates for the
Jamaica Local Examinations (First Year). In the whole island
there were 6,216 candidates and of these 1,487 gained passes. Of
this number only twenty-six received Class I passes, and the four
from this centre were included in the number! That year, first,
second and third places in the island were gained by these blind
scholars, with no concessions having been made for their lack of
sight. The point was proved, and in 1959 the establishment was
officially recognized as a special school by the Ministry of Education and from then on its teachers have been approved and
employed by the Ministry.

Each year thereafter, until the present time, a number of
candidates from the school have entered for local examinations
and have had phenomenal success—often gaining one hundred
per cent passes.

Although the rate of unemployment is very high in Jamaica,
a fair amount of success has been achieved in placing young
people in jobs. One totally blind young man is a fully qualified
physiotherapist, working in a local hospital. In 1962 he was
granted a Government Scholarship to the Royal National
Institute for the Blind School of Physiotherapy, in London, and
qualified at the end of three years as a Member of the Chartered
Society of Physiotherapists. Currently another young man is
following the same course and is in his final year. A further
student, a young woman who has complied with the entrance
requirements, anticipates shortly travelling to London to commence training.

The workshops for the blind (Salvation Army) provide
sheltered employment for quite a number who can undertake
machining, chair-caning and other crafts.

In the sewing room of the workshops today there is at least
one link with the early classroom, in Church Street, Kingston.
She is Estorah—one of the first young girls to come to Major

Barrell for tuition. A bright and eager girl, she soon learnt braille, but her practical disposition led her to ask Mrs. Barrell if she would teach her to sew—using a sewing machine. Mrs. Barrell agreed, and in next to no time Estorah was a competent machinist, able to sew skirts and blouses. Still Estorah was not satisfied—after all, there wasn't anything too unusual in a blind person using a sewing machine. ' Why shouldn't a blind person cut her own material to pattern? ' suggested Estorah. Even Mrs. Barrell was shocked at this suggestion; no, she hadn't ever heard of a blind person doing *that*!

But Estorah persisted in her idea. Unknown to Mrs. Barrell, she obtained some cloth and, at night when everyone else was in bed, Estorah would experiment with scissors and cloth. She used an ordinary tape measure marked at each inch with a staple. She used her own blouse as a pattern and, by deftly following the shape and outline, cut her cloth to the pattern. No sooner was the material cut out, than Estorah sat down at her machine and sewed the garment. Proudly next morning, she displayed her completed work to Mrs. Barrell, who was thrilled at Estorah's accomplishment. From that day Estorah began to cut all the blouses and dresses needed by pupils of the Institute for the Blind, and thus began a lifetime of useful service and employment.

Provision was also made for elderly blind persons in a new home on Westerham Estate. And in 1963–64 an experiment was made in the training of blind boys in agriculture. This was the Westerham Boys' Training Farm (later Williamsfield). The Salvation Army Williamsfield Training Farm School is training a number of blind and partially sighted boys in poultry farming and market gardening and it is hoped that this will be another successful avenue of employment.

In 1969 there was yet a further extension to the work, in the opening of a deaf-blind unit.

A german measles epidemic which swept the island of Jamaica in 1965 brought disastrous results. Mothers who contracted the disease during early pregnancy gave birth to severely handicapped babies whose varying combinations of poor vision, hearing loss and brain damage unfit them for training in any programme for the singly deaf or singly blind child. Thus, to meet this new demand, an officer and a teacher from the School for the Blind and Visually Handicapped received twelve months' specialized training at the Perkins School for the Blind, Watertown, Mass., U.S.A., returning to Kingston, where the deaf-blind unit was opened on September 29, 1969. Ten rubella children were initially accepted, some with pathetic backgrounds. . . . Someone called the new unit ' The school for the multiple-handicapped '.

The unit is at present helping ten such children. Of the two teachers who received a year's intensive, specialized training at Perkins School for the Blind and are now using their knowledge with skill and purpose, the one who is also an officer is the Matron of the unit and is busily engaged in training suitable young people to help in the care of the children.

Due to lack of accommodation, the deaf-blind unit is housed about seven miles from the school, but it is earnestly hoped that the building of a proposed new school will shortly commence, so that the hardships of teachers, working day by day so sacrificially for these little ones, may be eased.

In the Bahamas, Haiti and Panama there have also been blind persons who can be grateful to God for the work started by Colonel and Mrs. Barrell.

In recent years, at the suggestion of one of the officers working among them, a group of sightless people then being helped in the West Indies subscribed to a collection made for the purpose of sending flowers to Colonel and Mrs. Barrell in their retirement, as a tribute to the work these comrades had done on their behalf. By the time the letter bearing the money arrived in England, Mrs. Barrell had been promoted to Glory, but at the Colonel's suggestion the gift was put toward the erection of a memorial stone in a Birmingham Crematorium, bearing the words, ' In memory, from some of her blind friends in Jamaica '.

EAST AFRICA
Provision for the blind

It was two nursing sisters from a Nairobi Hospital who, because they were concerned about the problem of blindness in East Africa, first appealed to The Salvation Army for action. In Kenya alone an incidence of 55,000 cases of blindness had been estimated. ' Can anything be done for these people ? ' they asked. It seemed that here was an area of need being almost totally neglected.

They addressed their questions to the right person, for the Territorial Commander who received them at The Salvation Army's Territorial Headquarters in Nairobi and heard their pleas was Colonel John Barrell who, with Mrs. Barrell, had earlier been instrumental in the setting up of educational and training work for the blind in Kingston, Jamaica.

Following that initial proposal from the nursing sisters, a committee of interested people was formed, on which the Government Medical Department was represented; and The

Salvation Army began, as a result, to examine the possibility of setting up a similar institution in East Africa to that for which Colonel and Mrs. Barrell had been responsible in the West Indies.

In the meantime Mrs. Colonel Barrell, with the assistance of another officer-wife, Mrs. Colonel Chris. Widdowson, accepted responsibility for giving instruction in braille to two sightless young men at the Territorial Headquarters. As word spread of this innovation, other blind men arrived in numbers which quickly caused an overflow of available accommodation, and a move to the officer training college was undertaken.

In the meantime discussion of the problem with the Governor and educational and medical authorities led to the proposal to establish a residential institute for the blind. This proposal was realized in the opening, on January 6, 1944, of a centre at Thika, where Lieut.-Colonel (then Major) and Mrs. Edward Charles Osborne were given charge of the work, the first intake number- ing twenty-six students. During the following twelve years Lieut.-Colonel and Mrs. Osborne, together with their staff, toiled indefatigably to expand and improve both the facilities and scope of the school. The programme, at first geared mainly to voca- tional training, was gradually altered to become basically academic in character.

In 1955 the first sightless girls were accepted and vocational training in typewriting and telephone operating provided, which led to employment in open industry. By this time the number of pupils resident in the school was in the region of 150, with most following an eight-year programme of primary-level education on a curriculum closely parallel to that set for sighted school- children.

Subsequent years have seen a secondary school for the blind operating at Form IV stage, with a total of sixty pupils and several students attending Thika High School and studying for examinations at ' O ' or ' A ' levels. Others have taken courses in teacher training colleges. One pupil of the original intake has spent five years in the U.K., Canada and the U.S.A., and gained two degrees.

The School for the Blind at Thika stands on twenty-seven acres of ground and premises comprise fourteen class rooms, eleven dormitories, a sheltered workshop, domestic science, kindergarten, nursery administration, various dining rooms and kitchens, stores, dispensary, staff quarters, assembly hall, swim- ming pool and library.

The original institute at Thika is now ' mother ' to three other schools—the secondary school functioning under its own head-master and staff on the Thika compound; and that at Kibos, which provides a seven-year primary-level education programme and has some 120 children in residence; with the third at Likoni, which has reached standard five, with approximately sixty-five pupils in residence.

A number of national officers now supplements overseas officer-staff, and it is interesting to note that, with all the attendant development brought about in the past ten years, there is only the same number of *overseas* officers (staffing four institutions for more than 400 residents) as there were for the one school some ten years or so earlier.

Nursery and kindergarten departments have been an asset in preparing small children for the school stage. Many arrive in a lamentable state of neglect and it is a particular joy to the staff to see how quickly the marks of malcondition give place to evidence of good health and contentment as a result of consistent care and training in these departments.

An interesting development has come about in consequence of the school's emphasis on vocal and instrumental music. Not only has evangelical outreach been strengthened, with oppor-tunity for participation in programmes and meetings in schools, colleges, corps and community centres all over Kenya as well as in Uganda and Tanzania, but the music of the school has been featured prolifically in both sound and television broadcasts.

One big problem to be faced concerns employment-placing. 'To meet this there is a twofold need,' writes Major William Swansbury, formerly the Principal of the Thika Blind Institute, Kenya, and now the Assistant General Secretary for The Salvation Army's East Africa Territory. 'One, to provide vocational training programmes for school-leavers, so that the labour market can be offered at least semi-skilled employees in various trades. Secondly, there is need for a liaison service, which else-where is provided by placement officers whose knowledge of conditions in educational and industrial fields is the basis for introducing handicapped workmen to potential employers, and exercising supervision during the initial stage of adjustment to a new environment.

'The Salvation Army, in co-operation with others as well as by its own efforts, has done, and continues to do, something about the problem of blindness in East Africa,' Major Swansbury writes. 'The support of many people in many lands makes this work possible.' As he further points out, 'There is need for extension of educational facilities in the remoter regions, where the nomadic and primitive way of life produces a high incidence of blindness. Yet these districts are extremely difficult of access, and living conditions are very precarious. Education for *children without handicaps* has barely been introduced.

Institute for physically handicapped children

' Joytown ', at Thika, is an institute catering for approximately 200 boys and girls, who are mostly of school age and crippled. The majority are post-polio cases. From a medical standpoint the work is largely physiotherapy, and a resident physiotherapist, sponsored by the Voluntary Service Overseas Organization, conducts a remedial-exercise programme as part of the educational time-table. The centre provides an educational programme of seven years at primary level, and a degree of vocational training (in tailoring and typewriting) for a few of the older students. As its name indicates, the outlook of ' Joytown ' is hopeful and its aims are both positive and progressive.

Help for the destitute

There is a great need for amenities for the aged and destitute blind in East Africa and at one such centre, at Mgulani Camp, Dar es Salaam, where the work of providing residence and care has been started, the camp has, as part of its complex programme, a department for the care and welfare of crippled children, operating on similar lines to ' Joytown ', though with lesser emphasis on the provision of education facilities.

An institute for the destitute situated at Kiambu, near Nairobi, is called *Mji wa Huruma* (Town of Compassion). The residents are described as ' infirm, aged, mentally sub-normal and physically handicapped ', and this militates against a large-scale programme of rehabilitation. The object, primarily, is to provide an asylum of comfort and amenity as a measure of relief, though at Kiambu there is a limited degree of craft-work in sisal-mat weaving and the products are of a high standard and easily marketable.

Hostel for ambulant sick

There is a hostel for ambulant sick at Kampala, Uganda, which is laid out in wards something after the pattern of a small hospital. Here patients who have had limbs amputated and are awaiting supply of artificial limbs are accommodated.

NORTH-EASTERN INDIA
A very happy family
'Away up on the borders of India, in an area adjoining
Sikkim, Tibet, Bhutan and Nepal, lies the fascinating town of
Kalimpong. . . . The scenery is ruggedly beautiful. Thickly
wooded hills stretch far off into the distance, coursed by mountain
streams, soft and silent in summer, swiftly flowing, turbulent and
a menace to the plains folk during the rainy season. Mountain
ranges rise higher and higher until that mighty giant of the
Himalayas, Kanchanjunga, pushes its snowclad peak above
listless clouds.

' Yet amid such surroundings, on a hillside facing the practically unknown country of Sikkim, is a little oasis for boys and
girls who will never see the grandeur of nature that surrounds
them, never gaze on the fascinating figures in the bazaars. Though
blind, they are happy children, climbing the stepped mountain-
sides as surely as many sighted people who know the way.'

In 1940 the Hon. Mary H. H. Scott, M.B.E., a missionary who
had been an honorary worker of the Church of Scotland in
India since 1905, retired from active service. She was constrained
at that time to do something for the sightless and otherwise
handicapped children of the area she knew so well. (Her mission
had been among the hill people of Kalimpong, Kurseong,
Gangtok and Darjeeling.) Numbers of these children were blind
and destitute, and were to be found begging in the bazaars.
' Commencing with six blind handicapped boys, she founded an
institution for their care and education at Kalimpong, and in the
next twelve years seventy-one blind, crippled and otherwise
handicapped children, including three deaf mutes, were cared
for by "Aunt Mary ", as she was affectionately known.

' In 1953 she was led to ask The Salvation Army to take over
the work, and early in 1954 Major Hazel Koerner, now Mrs.
Brigadier Henry Watson (R.) of Yucca Valley, California, was
appointed to the Mary Scott Home for the Blind.'[24] While
negotiations were proceeding, Major Koerner worked for a time
with the home's original founder. 'Aunt Mary ' had prayed in
faith for someone to take her place and felt that the Salvation
Army officer was the answer to her prayer. The trust was
accepted by The Salvation Army in faith that support for the
work would be forthcoming.

The home is now in the charge of Brigadier Dorothy V. Page,
a Canadian officer. ' Today we have fifty students in the school,'
she wrote in 1970, ' with eight teachers, five of them blind. They

were our students, who have had proper training and are working in the school. Rehabilitation is a problem. We have, however, been able to train some boys as teachers in other schools. Two boys have earned B.A. degrees. One of these went to Perkins School for the Blind, and the other to England, for special training. They are now both on our staff. Last year we sent a boy to Bombay to study physiotherapy. This is a new field and a very good one.

' The children mostly come from poor homes and are unable to pay anything for their board. We feed, shelter, clothe and educate them, following exactly the same programme as a sighted school up to grade eight. The school is fully recognized by the Government.

' Music plays a great part. We hold open-air meetings in the market place. The people listen well. I am so proud of the fact that we have now enrolled seven Salvation Army soldiers and pray that more will be enrolled in the future. I did not want to push this, and I was thrilled when some asked me to arrange it. God has blessed us here, and we are a very happy family.'[24]

PAKISTAN

Hope is a sunrise

The Sunrise Institute for the Blind, in Lahore, West Pakistan, owes its existence to a large-hearted, determined lady named Marjory Fyson, who came to Pakistan in 1951 to engage in social welfare schemes for refugees. Her interest in the welfare of the blind was aroused, and this eventually led her to found the Pakistan Christian Blind Society with the help of sympathetic friends. She faced many near insuperable obstacles in her efforts to promote a system of training and rehabilitation for such handicapped children, but was ultimately successful in obtaining a suitable property, on the outskirts of Lahore city, that had formerly been an *ashram*.

Here, since 1958, the Sunrise Institute has played a noble role in making sightless young people adequate for active life. During the past ten years the institute has become the principal source of supply of Urdu braille material, and a workshop of ideas for the rehabilitation of the blind.

Both Muslim and Christian boys and girls are catered for and all normal subjects are taught as in a sighted school, except that handwork takes the place of drawing. Teachers, both blind and sighted, are fully trained and use the braille medium.

Handicrafts include the manufacture of string, string bags, stools, etc., as well as chair-caning and the making of bamboo ' chiks ' or screens.

Planned recreation has an important place and, apart from cricket played with a ball of thick brass with bits of metal inside it, there are team games such as running, hopping, relay and sack races and a tough kind of obstacle race. It is also considered important that the young people should visit places of interest and meet other people, so such outings are a regular feature. Music and singing also play an important part, and a well-run scout troop has an annual camp on its programme.

On her retirement, Miss Fyson expressed her desire that her work should be taken over by The Salvation Army—a tribute to the Army's international ministry in this field of human service. Mr. and Mrs. William Mayhew, a young Christian couple who had been working at the Army's Territorial Headquarters in Paris and desired some specialized work on the mission field, were brought to Lahore and have since given themselves for the welfare of these sightless young people. The Sunrise Institute must surely bring the ' sunrise ' of hope to the hearts of those it serves.[19]

HONG KONG

Because of local superstition and fears about ' devil-possession ', the handicapped or mentally-retarded child among the great population that throngs Hong Kong has a particularly difficult time. Many such children, abandoned by their parents, have found nowhere to live but on the streets, their condition pitiful and hard to imagine by any who have never seen the results of their ill-treatment by those who regard them with fear.

At the beginning of 1969 The Salvation Army became pioneers in a new field of social endeavour with the opening of a newly-renovated home for such mentally-retarded and crippled children. The home, situated on a hill on the small island of Cheung Chau, is reached by a one-hour journey on a ferry boat from Hong Kong itself, followed by a slow half-hour plod uphill.

An American officer, Brigadier Ethelmae Bilton, was appointed the first Administrator and, in a short time with a staff of eight workers, began to care for a group of twenty-seven children who were soon established in the newly-decorated rooms.

The Canada Territory has manifested a particular interest in the programme of care for these handicapped children: one room was donated by Hamilton Temple Corps, Ontario.

When Commissioner Clarence Wiseman, Territorial Commander for Canada, made a journey, with Mrs. Wiseman, to Cheung Chau Island during a visit to Hong Kong, they dedicated the building, at that time not yet occupied. But within a few months the air was filled with the laughter and singing of happy children. *The War Cry* in Canada gave publicity to the venture and showed photographs of the children, with the announcement—'A child like this one at Cheung Chau may be sponsored for $15.00 per quarter.' The Home League Department at Territorial Headquarters became a channel for help.

It was noted in *The War Cry* that within the first few weeks of the home being opened the children were responding to the warm and tender loving care being shown to them. Medical aid was offered by a small hospital on Cheung Chau Island, and it was recorded that a nurse was a full-time staff member of the home. ' The Government of Hong Kong has expressed its appreciation to the Army for initiating this programme,' said this early report, ' and the Director of Welfare was the guest speaker at the opening of the home.'

Chapter
Four

MINISTRY TO THE NEEDY IN THE SOUTH AMERICAN CONTINENT

BRAZIL

THOUGH Brazil is acknowledged to be a very rich country—rich in mineral and agricultural resources—and ranking as the world's fifth largest country in area, and seventh in population, it has its poverty-stricken areas and peoples, and from 1922, when pioneer officers, Lieut.-Colonel and Mrs. David Miche, unfurled the Salvation Army flag in Rio, the poor and suffering have been the concern of Salvationists and their friends in that land. Lieut.-Colonel Richard Christensen, of Denmark, one of the pioneer officers, has told of his own experiences in Pôrto Alegre, where with his wife he was appointed in December, 1935, and describes the need apparent in that area. He writes:

'A doctor of medicine and his wife were among our first converts. . . . Our visitation work in the slum districts revealed to us the extreme misery and the hopelessness of sick people. Many of them were old, abandoned in their huts, living on straw mats on the floor, often in great pain. Many suffered from terrible diseases and were starving. Some had no money, no family, no friends, and no hope of medical treatment.

' Our new convert, the doctor, visited and helped a number of them, but I pointed out to him our responsibility as Christians to do more for those poor miserable and sick people. He began to pray over this question and finally he and his wife decided that he should give up his practice for a few years and dedicate his skill, love and strength, to help the poor.

' What a happy day it was for my wife and myself when he told us this good news! Without delay, we started preparations for a medical mission. We knew where to find those in the greatest need of medical aid, and what a joy it was for us to take the doctor to them, and then to see the results of his treatment.'[25]

' Our plan, when we started the work in South Brazil, was to train people to help themselves and not to depend upon help from outside. This was difficult, but by the grace of God, to a certain degree we succeeded. Our medical mission, children's homes and other activities, such as our day schools for poor children, received very little help from outside the State of Rio Grande do Sul.

'All the departments had to learn to find people in their districts who would give monthly or three-monthly subscriptions as members of our " helping brigades ".'[26]

(When a great part of Pôrto Alegre was inundated during serious floods in the early days of The Salvation Army's work in Brazil, the doctor was very busy giving necessary medicine and treatment. Such service brought its own appreciation from recipients and Salvation Army benefactors alike. There were Government requests to help the inhabitants when the floods were over.) ' The task was a great one, and our helpers were few,' writes Lieut.-Colonel Christensen, ' but I later reported to the Government that the inhabitants in Ilhota had received aid that they needed. The dirt was cleansed away from the houses and streets; all had received mattresses, bed-clothes and all necessary clothes to wear. The doctor had examined the people living in the Ilhota, and work was provided for the men. We had opened a day-school . . . where all the poor children received books etc. free. We started instruction for the mothers in our home league.'[27]

In 1967 the faithful Dr. Leopoldo Rössler, of Brazil, was admitted to The Salvation Army's order of Distinguished Auxiliary Service, the citation for which reads: 'For thirty years as founder and tireless patron of the Medical Clinic in Navegantes, Pôrto Alegre, ministering to thousands of sick people.'

A course of instruction in social work, begun in the early days and in which the doctor and his wife offered part-time help in training nurses, attracted a young woman by the name of Raquel, who felt that God was calling her to give all her time to help the sick and the poor. In spite of her father's rabid opposition and his threat to disown her, she felt she must obey God's call. Lieut.-Colonel Christensen writes, 'During the years she stayed with us, she became a teacher in the home league, and studied nursing and slum work.

'We mention Raquel . . . because we have never known a more self-denying woman. Sometimes she was told by the doctors to be more careful for her own health, when she nursed patients who had terrible contagious diseases. But she always said: "I am in God's service, and He is able to keep me."[27]

'Sometimes she passed many days and nights with such patients, but she was never contaminated. When her lame patients became a little better, she took them out in a [wheel] chair, into the sunshine, and she was happy.

'When Raquel entered a poor hut where a mother was sick, she took charge of everything. She dressed the children, sending them to our day-school. If the husband was without work, she phoned to the factories to get work for him. She was faithful and diligent until her last day, when God called her to His eternal mansions.'[28]

Lieut.-Colonel Christensen writes convincingly about his views on countries in a state of development, countries which need the help that others can give them. He says: 'I am convinced that the western world's existence in future will depend on the help given to countries in evolution. Anybody reading the statistics of the United Nations will look with terror on the hundreds of millions who are starving, sick, in despair and pain in the lands in evolution. We who are living in so-called Christian lands, having all we need, have a tremendous responsibility, not only to give economic, technical and other material help to them, but we need also to think about our responsibility before God, to send missionaries to preach the gospel to them.

'All of us, without exception, have a holy duty to send out the right kind of people to the lands in evolution, as missionaries,

technicians in industry and agriculture, as well as teachers to open
schools, and doctors and nurses '.[29]

*   *   *

The Salvation Army Medical Clinic in Campinas, Brazil, was
opened in May, 1953, in this progressive centre of 295,000
inhabitants situated some fifty miles from São Paulo. Campinas
has various industries, some introduced from overseas (chiefly
North America) which have established their factories in the city,
thus increasing the number of workers who are among those The
Salvation Army tries to help.

The following is an extract from *Brado de Guerra* (' The War
Cry ') of August 22, 1953, reporting the inauguration of the
Clinic:

' Campinas Corps takes another step, opening the doors of a
medical clinic for consultations, medicines, injections and medical
dressings for needy people.

' We are happy that the poor can now find relief for their
physical pains, as far as medical science allows.

' Dr. Antonio Melone Sobrinho is doing efficient work as
physician and is gaining the affection of all who come to our
institution. We express to him our thanks, and hope that he will
stay with us for a long time, having the same success as has
already been attained.

' Sergeant Izabel Godio, having served for many years at the
" Beneficencia Portuguesa ", has the qualities of an experienced
nurse and is at present our dedicated and constant helper, with
sole responsibility in that capacity.

' Corps Cadet Ezir Maia takes care of the file and ably fulfils
this task. We pray God's richest blessing upon these comrades as
recompense for their selfless service. It is our desire that the clinic
in Campinas may attend all the needy who come to us, always with
the motto: *Saved to Serve!* '

The clinic is operated by the officers of Campinas Corps,
which was itself opened on October 30, 1929. A small charge is
made for a consultation, but in cases of poverty, services are given
free. The medical attendants are voluntary and at present are
Dr. Donald Gordon and Dr. Maphalia Price, both Americans.

A short time ago a dental clinic was also commenced with the
help of Dr. Henry MacKnight, formerly of the Peace Corps,
U.S.A.

An important feature of the clinic is the fact that the dentist and doctors work hand in hand. In a number of cases where health has been impaired by dental decay, patients are immediately referred to the dentist and, with the joint efforts of the two professionals, make a speedy recovery.

In many cases of extreme poverty it is possible, in the customary Salvation Army way, to help with clothing, food, and so on, the needs of the patients being as many and varied as the colour of their skins. From those with minor ailments to those suffering from major illnesses, all are treated with the utmost care and individual attention.

Many of the patients travel great distances to attend the clinic, some staying with friends overnight in order to do so, because it is well known in the area that our doctors *care* and give a great deal of time to each person, unlike some who prescribe on spoken word without making any examination.

Some of the patients arrive soon after 7 a.m., although the clinic does not open until 9 a.m. Devotions are conducted with staff and patients before the busy morning begins; and how they love to sing!

' The main difficulty is the fact that our medical clinic is open for only one day per week and every person must make an appointment,' says a report. ' On one occasion, not long ago, the books had to be closed because bookings were all filled up for the next five months. For a person who is really ill to have to wait all that time to see the doctor seems somewhat ridiculous.'

Like any other clinic, that in Campinas admits to failures as well as claiming successes, but naturally success stories are preferred. One such is about Senhor Abel, a man from humble surroundings, but one who knows how to work—and to work hard—to support his wife and six children. He arrived at the clinic one morning after leaving home at sunrise to make the thirty-mile trip. He had had the misfortune to fall whilst working and had injured his spine. After some weeks of treatment he was feeling much better, and as his faith in the doctor increased, so did the number of his consultations, for he brought with him each time yet another member of his family until all (including his wife) had been examined and treated by the doctor! On his final visit, Senhor Abel was a changed man, full of hope and with a new desire for life. He had indeed passed through hard times. There had been no money at all coming into the home, and the entire family were in need of medical attention, but here at the clinic he had found people who cared, who gave free medicines, treatment, and even some food and clothing for his children: this indeed was a different world from any which he had previously known.

'Most of our cases come into four categories: worms, heart complaints, blood pressure and the many and varied illnesses stemming from malnutrition,' says the report. 'For these particular cases we are never able to keep up the supply of medicines. During recent times there has been an upsurge in epileptic cases. The reason for this we do not know. The many types of attack and the need for individual research into each case to find the right medicine, can at times mean rather slow progress for some of the patients.

'The story of Maria comes to mind. A young woman of twenty-three years, she had at least three epileptiform attacks daily from the time she was a few days old. Only in recent months, and after a great deal of persuasion, her father had brought her along for treatment. A rather selfish man, although he received a good sum of money each month from a former employer, he begrudges the few *cruzeiros* to buy the prescribed medicines for his daughter. When Maria takes the necessary pills her attacks are greatly reduced, but then her father decides she no longer needs the drugs and we begin our story all over again! At the moment this cannot be called a success story, as Maria's progress is stationary because of her father's ignorance. Medical care for this girl is not the only thing needed—a teaching programme for her father is also required. One day we shall win through.'

All the money involved, the hours of work entailed—are they worth it? The officers at Campinas think so. When they see a patient arrive, weighed down with problems, and after some weeks see that same patient as a new person, with a new outlook and a wider horizon, somewhere within there arises that 'feeling of usefulness', for here, through the clinic, people are finding a new purpose in living.

'Our aim, of course,' say the officers, 'is not only to heal the sick, but to introduce them to the Lord Jesus Christ, the Great Physician.'

ARGENTINA

In the year 1939, Mr. Mayon, the owner of a big dental company in Buenos Aires, provided the necessary equipment to open a small dental clinic at the Salvation Army Headquarters building. Ever since, the company has provided most of the material needed and paid the professional fees of the senior dental surgeon.

From the beginning, Dr. Jorge Martinez has been in charge of the first consulting room. Soon afterwards a second one was opened in an office in the Army's eventide home for men in another sector of Buenos Aires. This home is near a large abbatoir and meat-packing factory and has always catered for the men and their families who are workers there. The equipment here was also provided by the Company Mayon, and Dr. Martinez gives the same professional service.

In June 1960, Dr. Martinez was awarded the Order of Distinguished Auxiliary Service for his many years of dedicated and untiring service to the needy. He is a golf fan and many of the boys who have ' caddied ' for him have been invited to avail themselves of his dental services at the Salvation Army clinics.

In more recent years, Dr. Edith Schnoerr has joined the dental staff and has attended in the Headquarters clinic, as well as at a new centre opened in connection with The Salvation Army's primary school in a shantytown, where more than 500 children attend the seven grades and two kindergartens. These have all been checked for dental attention and as much work as possible has been done for them. Until recently, the centre had only a foot pedal drill, while the actual dental chair is only an iron chair with a plastic-covered box set on it, to make it high enough for small heads to reach the head-rest which has been attached!

The law requires a dental certificate for all children who attend The Salvation Army's school and for those in the children's home; and the Ministry of Education sends round regular inspectors who make the necessary recommendations on the dental needs of each child. The school or institution is responsible to see that these are followed up, but in the cases where the child has one parent who works, and pays what he or she can for the child in the home, we cannot insist they take the youngster to the dentist, and constantly ask for time off from their own work in order to do so. Neither are they in a position to pay a private dentist. This problem has brought about the need to employ a further dentist, Dr. Beatriz Herbel. She also attends in our Headquarters clinic, and will be replacing Dr. Martinez when he officially retires. At the moment the situation involves bringing the children from the home to the clinic in Buenos Aires. There are sixty-five of them and nearly all need at least a minimum of attention.

The three dental clinics exist to meet the needs of people who cannot afford to pay dental bills, and provide a service they would not otherwise have. Though there is no record of men and women who have actually been converted through this work, all the waiting rooms are provided with Gospels, copies of *The War Cry* and Bibles that the people can take away if they wish; and many have been distributed in this way.

There are many *villas de emergencia* (shantytowns) in and around Buenos Aires, and various corps have work in them. It seems that when men and women and young people are converted in the meetings in the *villas*, they are anxious to improve their homes as well as their own personal appearance, and this results in their coming to see one of the dentists at the Salvation Army clinic. There have been several cases where a new soldier has appeared with her new uniform and new dentures simultaneously! The recognition of need for dental care seems to come with their spiritual growth.

By December 22, 1970, the number of patients who had attended the clinic at the Headquarters building was recorded as 43,600.

*   *   *

From 1929 to 1958 a maternity clinic was operated for women of modest means. 'Bethesda', as it was called, had a very high standing, and women from Patagonia and other distant parts of Argentina travelled to Buenos Aires to be attended there. Dr. Guismondi, a well-known professional, was the director there until the time of his passing.

The spiritual tone and atmosphere of the clinic was much appreciated and daily devotions in the rooms were welcomed by Catholics and Jews, as well as Evangelicals.

This well-known clinic had to be closed in 1958 because of difficulties that had much to do with problems of the country at the time.

Chapter **MEDICAL WORK IN**
Five **AFRICA**

BRIGADIER SIDNEY GAUNTLETT, reviews Salvation Army medical work in Africa:

As with many Christian missions to Africa, Salvation Army pioneers first landed at Cape Town. These early Salvationists, like others, then worked their way northward, crossing the

Limpopo river to what is now Rhodesia, in 1891. Salvationist activities were taken across the Zambezi into Northern Rhodesia (now Zambia) in 1924. At about the time that the Zambezi was crossed, Salvationist missionaries landed in disease-infested West Africa—Nigeria and the Gold Coast (later Ghana)—and also in East Africa, to develop work in these countries.

Later still, in the 1930's, The Salvation Army began a virile work in what was the Belgian Congo and French Equatorial Africa. In all these countries, except for the Congo and Equatorial Africa, there was an interval of twenty to forty years or more before any organized medical work was started.

This is, of course, no indication of lack of concern, and during this period all missionaries provided simple medical care as they travelled the long distances—usually on foot or by ox-cart—across the African bush from village to village. The passport of a good missionary could be said to be a Bible and a set of dental forceps. Many learned the art of tooth-pulling, wound dressing and the dispensing of simple medicines from their colleagues—the healer learned, and the healed suffered, the hard way! A number of our Salvation Army missionaries were fortunate enough to have training at the Livingstone College in London.

Not until 1929—forty-six years after The Salvation Army set foot on the continent of Africa—did the first trained nurses arrive to take up appointment at what is now the William Eadie Maternity Hospital in Vendaland—a remote and backward area of South Africa.*

Help for scattered populations

The vast distances and sparsely scattered populations create problems in providing even elementary medical care for the people. With the exception of the Congo—Kinshasa and Brazzaville—medical centres have always been established in the rural areas, often quite remote from a town and other hospitals or clinics. This has meant that although most of these centres are quite small, and without a doctor, they have to cope with almost any medical problem—at least by providing first aid treatment.

Communications today are, in general, improved; but for many years nurses had to undertake many tasks for which their training did not prepare them—including complicated maternity procedures and minor surgery. Local girls, and in some cases boys, were trained in elementary nursing care and in a few centres,

* See Training programmes ', p. 122.

like the Catherine Booth and Mountain View Hospitals, in South
Africa—and the clinics, in Congo-Brazzaville—a definite nurse
training programme, which is not recognized by the Government,
has been carried out. Only at the Howard Hospital in Rhodesia,
and the Chikankata Hospital in Zambia, are there government-
recognized training courses, and in both cases these were started
shortly after the opening of the hospitals.

Beginnings were simple

Most of the Salvation Army work in Africa today consists of
small dispensaries or clinics, usually in the charge of a non-
national officer-nurse. This has been the pattern from the
beginning, and only in a few instances has a small unit developed
into a larger hospital with facilities to cope with a wide range of
medical conditions. Beginnings were quite simple, and even
primitive, in most areas—a cottage or box room converted into a
simple dispensary, or daily dispensing of one or two standard
mixtures, and simple dressing of wounds, conducted from the
back door of the missionary's house. Usually the wife became the
nurse and both she and her husband had to be prepared for the
occasional unheralded maternity case.

A simple hut, where medicines could be kept and dressings
more easily carried out, would be the next stage. Sometimes this
was as far as development proceeded. Most of the present buildings are of permanent brick and have reasonable facilities. The
extent to which a medical centre has developed appears to have
depended upon the availability of funds—for both building and
maintenance—local medical need, and government medical
policy.

Varying rates of development

Where it is the Government's policy to subsidize Christian
medical work, as is the case in South Africa, Rhodesia, Ghana,
Zambia and East Africa, a better standard than elsewhere of
building and equipment has usually been possible. This explains
some discrepancy between rate of development and local need
when comparing one country with another. In a number of
countries, including South Africa, Rhodesia, Zambia and Congo-
Kinshasa, medical work has been developed alongside schools
with the establishment of ' mission stations '. Elsewhere there
is often a divisional headquarters (from where district evangelical
work is directed) close to the dispensary.

The type of work undertaken tends to vary according to the country, the initial pattern becoming the tradition. For example, in Ghana most of our medical work is midwifery, with a number of well run but small clinics serving a wide area; in South Africa there is some emphasis upon maternity and tuberculosis work, whilst in East Africa the emphasis is on rehabilitation—of the blind and crippled. Salvation Army medical work in Congo-Kinshasa and Congo-Brazzaville consists of small clinics in quite modern buildings offering out-patient treatment only, but extensive village work, leading in some cases to the use of mobile dispensaries.

In Rhodesia and Zambia there is well-developed general medical and surgical work, with an emphasis on training in two centres. These two centres were for some years the only Salvation Army hospitals in Africa with a doctor; and for many years there was only one Salvation Army doctor in the whole of Africa— that is, at Chikankata. This latter hospital has the only leprosy work run by The Salvation Army in Africa, and this began because the Government health department was seeking a leprosy treatment centre in that part of the country and, in faith, the hospital staff rose to the challenge. For some time the leprosy settlement there was the largest in the country.

Liaison with Governments

During most of our history in Africa there has been close liaison between Christian medical missions and the Government of the various countries. This has taken the form of financial support—for buildings, equipment and drugs in some countries— assistance from government medical officers, and co-operation with public health schemes, tuberculosis and leprosy control, vaccination programmes and, more recently, health education.

For example, the hospital at Chikankata, in Zambia, developed from a thirty-five-bed hospital to a 250-bed hospital with training schools and leprosy settlement with 400 patients in the space of twenty years, with almost all the capital cost of building and equipment being met by the Government and various local and overseas trusts.

In South Africa one of our centres could treble its capacity and add such facilities as an operating theatre, X-ray unit, recognized nurses' training school and provision for two doctors and proportionately increased staff—all at the expense of the Government, *if* The Salvation Army could find the professional staff to operate such a hospital.* Similar development would be possible at other South African centres were the necessary staff available.

Blind school work in East Africa has expanded considerably during the past few years with help from the Government.†

The effect of Independence upon this co-operation, in those countries that have become independent African states, has varied. In general, the desire for co-operation has been maintained and, in some instances, enhanced. The expression of help may have altered and circumstances associated with the change of administration have had their effect.

In Zambia there has been improved co-operation since Independence, with considerably increased financial support to medical missions. This has been made possible by a more affluent economy, with more revenue from the copper mines now staying in the country.

In both the Congos, government financial support ceased after Independence was achieved, probably due to the weakened economy of the country rather than a lack of willingness.

In Ghana there have been administrative problems which have resulted in restrictions on the medical practice undertaken by nurses in charge of our clinics. They are legally no longer entitled to give injections or administer certain essential drugs, such as antibiotics, without the prescription of a doctor. This has created considerable difficulties and imposed an added strain upon our nurses even though the difficulties are gradually being overcome.

Resourcefulness in isolated areas

The marked shortage of doctors—gradually being remedied—in the two Congos, following the attainment of Independence, has imposed a heavy responsibility on the nurses in charge of dispensaries, which are often quite isolated and to which many quite sick patients come for treatment. Poor roads and the absence of telephone communication at most of the clinics add to the isolation. An idea of the problems faced will be given by the history of the Yangui Dispensary in Equatorial Africa (Congo-Brazzaville). This centre is seventy miles from the nearest town and fifteen miles from the nearest doctor, but is a hospital with nearly fifty beds—and has only one fully trained, non-national nurse. In 1951 Major Genevieve de Sarron, a French officer-nurse, with the help of only her patients and their relatives, made

* A Salvationist, Dr. David Senior, with his wife, a nurse, has been appointed (1971) for three years to the Catherine Booth Hospital.

† See 'Fresh hope for the handicapped', p. 154.

the bricks and built a new dispensary with a room at one end which became her living quarters. Her nursing training had taught her to lay operating theatre trolleys but not bricks, to paint infected wounds but not walls, but it was as well that her training had taught her resourcefulness! And she is typical of many other nurses who give devoted service under great strain and with many difficulties.

Short and long term service

Until recent years, trained medical personnel have all been Salvation Army officers, but with the increasing demands throughout the world, and the recognition of the value of non-officer staff, a number of non-officer Salvationist and non-Salvationist nurses, doctors and technicians have come forward and given valuable service, usually on a three-year contract basis, but some for longer terms. The doctor until recently in charge of the largest of our African hospitals was a Canadian Baptist. Medical staff come from countries throughout the world. With the development of the African countries, a gradually increasing proportion of the staff are nationals.

Prevention of Disease

Having in mind the vast needs of this continent and the very limited medical resources, it is increasingly recognized that the soundest medical policy is to concentrate upon prevention of disease rather than build up costly and elaborate curative services —which nevertheless are essential in order to treat established but curable disease and to win the people's confidence so that they will accept the preventive measures.

For some years, therefore, increasing emphasis has been placed upon a mobile service—whether by motor vehicle or bicycle—over a wide area around the smaller clinic or dispensary, with ante-natal and child welfare clinics, provision of preventive inoculations and the promotion of an active health education programme, in both base hospital or clinic and the surrounding villages. This will undoubtedly be the pattern during the coming years, with an increasing co-operation with the government health services.

In most countries there seems little likelihood of the Government taking over mission medical services in the foreseeable future, mainly because of the efficiency and greater economy of this service, but also because in most African countries there are insufficient government medical personnel to continue the work.

What of the future?

Throughout the history of Salvation Army medical work in Africa, the ministry of healing and a spiritual ministry—through dedicated Christian living and the proclamation of the living word of God—have gone hand in hand. The concept of man as body, mind and spirit makes this comprehensive approach essential but whilst, hitherto, our medical work has been ' imported ' from overseas, with the growing strength of the local Christian community, it must increasingly become an expression of their Christian love and concern for their fellows. This demands a greater measure of local financial support and administrative and professional responsibility, made possible through the development of the training programme for national personnel.

Chapter   # MEETING PRESENT
Six   # NEEDS IN INDIA

' I WANT the freedom of my country,' Gandhi once wrote about India, ' so that other countries may learn something from my free country, so that the resources of my country might be utilized for the benefit of mankind.'

' My patriotism is not an exclusive theory,' he declared. ' It is all-embracing.'

' For the benefit of mankind '; ' all-embracing '; Mahatma Gandhi, like all truly great seers, perceived that ' all life, in whatever form it appears, must be essentially one '.

Today free India, wrestling with the problem of national identity and self-responsibility, is discovering, like many another nation, how interdependent mankind is. Similarly the Christian Church, its medical services in particular, is finding the need to operate collectively ' for the benefit of mankind '. In the West there are nations ready to give financial and other help to developing countries. Health services in such countries should be able to benefit, but what and where are the areas of greatest need, and how can aid be most beneficially applied?

In 1969 it was estimated that the churches collectively—Roman Catholic, Protestant and Orthodox—were currently operating 628 medical institutions in India and that ninety-five per cent of the Christian medical work was devoted to curative institutions. It was an epoch-making event when, in January of that year, there was consultation at Bangalore by Roman Catholic and Protestant Church representatives to consider the future of Christian medical work in India. This had come about following a survey carried out by the World Council of Churches Committee on Specialized Assistance for Social Projects (S.A.S.P.) following a request made by the National Christian Council of India (N.C.C.I.) in 1966. The most serious of the deficiencies revealed by the survey had been ' the lack of mechanism for joint planning with central and state Governments '. It was therefore logical that the most far-reaching recommendation made at Bangalore was that a *Co-ordinating Board for Christian health services in India* be formed, with a full-time Secretary and other staff. The name has since been changed to the Christian Agency for Hospital Planning, and it will be made as widely representative as possible with sub-committees and a panel of technical advisers.

As the Government of India is by constitution secular, the possibility of grants to sectarian hospitals, whether Christian or otherwise is limited, apart from the fields of leprosy and tuberculosis, where Christian missionaries carry a major part of the total medical responsibility. The setting up of voluntary hospitals on a State level is therefore now advised and, encouraged by the Government, Christian organizations will be able to play an active role in this new development.

At the Bangalore consultation one critical observer said that Christian medical work in India as a whole appeared to be ' an unplanned, unco-ordinated operation, without clear objectives, trying unrealistically to meet needs which have not been properly assessed, in the face of a severe limitation of resources '.

Some realistic appraisals of the current situation were made, and speakers faced hard facts with courage, and a determination to plan accordingly. It was recommended that ' one immediate function of the Board would be to screen health-related applications going to funding agencies ' [i.e. bodies prepared to finance certain defined projects]. Projects would be judged ' *on the basis of principles set forth by the board* with the assistance of regional advisers and a panel of experts '.

The Ecumenical Press Service headed its hand-out on the decision taken at the Consultation, ' India's Christian hospitals take first step to co-operation '.

The committee recommended the ' need for a completely new stance in Christian medical service '. The emphasis would now have to be on ' Planning for Health Care ', with the following objectives:

(1) Comprehensive health care for people.
(2) Functional co-ordination of facilities.
(3) Cost-benefit analysis in determining priorities.
(4) Education and communication in line with objectives.
(5) Evaluation of effectiveness.
(6) Advisory services for improving programmes.
(7) Co-operation with Government.
(8) Public relations.

' There is a need to consider the role of Christian medical work in relation to the total understanding of *the service and witness of the Church*', was one of the findings. And another: ' There is also a need for education of Church leaders and members as well as medical workers in relation to *the healing task of the Church.*'

In summarizing the situation in India, and forecasting the role of Christian work, it was opined: ' Forgetting the identity of single institutions, and embarking on functional co-operation, it will be possible to offer our resources as a contribution to the efforts of Government. The development in relation to family planning, T.B. and leprosy was pointed out as encouraging examples in this direction. . . . There must be stress on Indianization as our activities are integrated with those of the Government into planning for comprehensive health care.'

A particularly striking picture of the situation as the committee saw it was provided by the statement:

' New directions in the development of health care and medical education point toward *a more comprehensive approach to man's needs*. This is more than just some attention to preventive medicine or health education. *It is a radical change of concept, looking at the community as the patient, and seeing the social pathology as the context of individual pathology*. We need to educate the medical profession and others (including Church leaders) to this new concept. . . .

' The Church must exercise a sense of stewardship, making available optimum health *within the economic reach of the people* in such a way that it is viable and clinically efficient at low cost* and seeks to serve the community rather than only individuals, thereby trying to create a new community in Christ.'

In popular reportage—' Our goal should be *to develop healthy*

* See T.A.L.C. (' Teaching Aids at Low Cost ', p. 179).

communities. This is *in contrast to building a wall around our compound and waiting for people to fall ill and come to us for repair.* Rather we should in limited areas, according to our capacity and personnel, go out to teach and assist our people to observe the laws of health, hygiene and nutrition, and to use the preventive measures necessary to maintain health. They will thus have less need of the expensive in-patient services of hospitals. This community ideal calls for a more comprehensive approach to health problems, involving relationship to socio-economic, cultural, agricultural, nutritional and environmental factors which contribute to the health of the community.'

Colonel (Dr.) Daniel Andersen attended the Conference of British Missionary Societies held at Edinburgh House, London, on April 14, 1969, following on the Bangalore Consultation.

This conference observed: ' No hospital as such improves the health of the community outside. The Church is being asked to look again at how it should express its healing ministry. It is facing increasing dilemmas: the economic situation, the changing clientéle being served—more and more the wealthy, which is inevitable where fee-for-service hospitals are operated and charity care decreasing—this is part of the universal problem.'

Having considered the emphasis on health care, among its recommendations the conference put forward the following:

' For the sake of the integrity of their help to Christian medical service in India, this meeting *recommends* that British missionary bodies *accept a co-ordinating body for Christian health services in India, with authority to evaluate priorities in capital support and to develop a process of education* to help Christian bodies in India toward a new understanding of Christian medical service. It further *recommends* that *missionary bodies in Britain should give capital grants only to projects approved by such a co-ordinating body in India.*'

Dr. (now Captain) Walter Lucas, Chief Medical Officer at The Salvation Army's MacRobert Hospital, Dhariwal, and Major Kathleen Brown, Matron of the same hospital, attended a Conference of Heads of Christian Hospitals and Dispensaries in the Christian Medical College and Hospital, Ludhiana, on April 23, 1969. Here a co-ordinating committee for the region (H.P. Jammu and Kashmir, Jandk, Punjab, Haryana and Delhi) was set up. Major Brown was nominated a member, as Nursing Representative. Part of the function of the committee is ' to be an evaluating committee in regard to grants for projects and to make reports on them to the Central Board in Delhi ', that is, the Co-ordinating Board for Christian Health Services in India.

To member churches of the National Christian Council of India a communication in the same month from the Executive Secretary, referring to the survey by S.A.S.P. following the request by the N.C.C.I. to the World Council of Churches in 1966, pointed out: ' The most serious among the deficiencies revealed by the survey is the lack of mechanization for joint planning with central and state Governments which are now increasingly emphasizing the need for *broad based community-centred health services concerned with the health of all people*, rather than concentrating on the episodic treatment of patients.'

Arising out of consultations in Holland and the Christian Agency for Hospital Planning in New Delhi, a comprehensive community health project has been sanctioned and submitted to the inter-church agency in Holland by Captain Walter Lucas, F.R.C.S., the Chief Medical Officer at Dhariwal Hospital. While the Punjab is called the granary of India because of its good irrigation, the majority of homes are constructed of mud, straw and cow-dung, and often shared with the domestic animals.

There is only one doctor per 6,000 population (which is better than in many other parts of India and elsewhere), and the infant mortality rate is 81 per 1,000 live births. Two-thirds of these infant deaths occur within the first month and *are preventable*, the most prevalent causes being tetanus and pulmonary tuberculosis.

Similar programmes are being prepared for each of our main hospitals in India. We have had the valuable voluntary help of Mr. A. Nielsen Warren, a Salvationist architect, who recently visited four of them and submitted plans and recommendations.

Chapter
Seven

WHAT OF TOMORROW?

BY conference and experiment, Christian bodies are severally working out what can and should be their contribution ' for the benefit of mankind ' in India, and elsewhere, in the future.

Here are some of the steps being taken by The Salvation Army in co-operation with other organizations:

Tropical Health Manual

The *Tropical Health Manual*, originally prepared by Dr. Percy Turner—and later revised by Dr. Wm. Noble in 1935, 1942 and by Dr. Daniel Andersen in 1961—is again being revised, with three new chapters to be included on salient needs of the future: (1) Care in pregnancy and childbirth; (2) Birth control teaching and (3) Towards community health. (The latter will consist of a series of lectures or talks suitable for delivery at home leagues (women's meetings) and to cadets in training for Salvation Army officership, as well as to young people at high school, and designed to give information on the foundations of community health.)

T.A.L.C.

Advantage is to be taken of suitable teaching aids as planned by Dr. David Worley at the Institute of Child Health, University of London, and known as T.A.L.C. (Teaching Aids at Low Cost) for use in education programmes. The material—specially designed to assist those studying and teaching child health—is 'particularly designed for those countries in the Tropics and Sub-Tropics where child health services in rural areas are still limited'. (The supply of these teaching aids at, or below, cost price has been made possible through grants from the Commonwealth Foundation and Oxfam.)

Among the aids are sets of colour slides and flannelgraphs. Most sets of slides number twenty-four and cover a variety of subjects, including child care, nutrition, identification of the commoner diseases and contraception. Easy-to-use weight charts have been developed for use in the under-fives' clinic in a design approved by international health organizations.

As soon as these facilities became known to them, Salvationists of the Croydon Citadel Corps—one of the oldest in The Salvation Army—made a donation of £100 for the provision of teaching aids at low cost. (It will be recognized that donations earmarked for use in this field 'go farther' because of the concessionary prices arranged at the source of supply.)

A Home League Manual

Through the home league, its world-wide women's movement, The Salvation Army has, since 1907, sought to minister to the needs of women, their homes and families, in many lands. In developing countries practical courses on child care, hygiene, nutrition and homecraft have long formed part of the home league's education programme.

A *Home League Manual*, issued by International Headquarters in 1949, followed a *Home League Primer*, published in 1946 ' for missionary lands '. Both of these publications contained, among other teaching, simple ' child welfare ' and ' health and hygiene ' instruction, designed to guide women living in fairly primitive conditions, though the later *Manual* was described as ' primarily designed to meet the needs of missionary officers with home league members possessing a measure of educational advantage, somewhat above that of the totally illiterate women of the villages, and for whom parts of the *Home League Primer* are thus not altogether suitable '.

Now, with the proposed issue of a new Manual, instructive lessons on community health in its various aspects are being prepared by Mrs. Colonel Sölvi Andersen, M.D. (Oslo), with a view to helping women in the changing circumstances of today to safeguard the health of their community by attention to the needs of their own families and those of their neighbourhood.

Hospitals as points of outreach

It is hoped that our hospitals will, where possible, be able to use members of the community at village level, under medical direction, to combat malnutrition, food and water infection and other ills. In this way hospitals will continue to extend the area of their usefulness.

Colonel (Dr.) Daniel Andersen has written (1969): ' The Salvation Army has five general hospitals in India, varying in size from 100–200 beds, with one exception, which has about 350. All of these hospitals have a *Nurses' Training School* recognized by Government with full recognition for the State Registered Course in four, and registered for Assistant Nurses and Midwives Course in the fifth.

' *One important current emphasis in the development of public health nursing, involving visits to health centres in the surrounding area. This will encourage an outreach from the hospital, which is essential.*

'Another aspect of the work of training schools for nurses and technicians is that they provide an opportunity for future service to young people, both Christian and non-Christian, which in the majority of cases will lead to work outside the training mission hospital and extend the Christian witness widely. As an example of this we have at Dhariwal, in North India, a well-organized school for medical technicians, run for about twenty years by a highly qualified Canadian missionary (Brigadier Ruth Woolcott), providing a diploma recognized both in mission and government hospitals. As a result, trainees from this centre, which is a relatively small missionary hospital with 100 beds, are found in government and mission institutions throughout the whole of the Punjab and in Delhi.'

Within The Salvation Army, the support of home leagues in the more favoured parts of the world for their less fortunate contemporaries in other lands has often been noteworthy. Missionary hospitals have long acknowledged the debt they owe to them. Today their generosity is being used to advance hospital outreach, as the following report to New Zealand from Captain (Dr.) Melvin Brieseman, of the Evangeline Booth Hospital, Ahmednagar, shows:

' The main bulk of donations from Whakatane, Milton and Upper Hutt Home Leagues went to purchase a puppet show. . . . In the villages there is very little in the way of entertainment—no TV, no picture theatres, no portable transistor radio. So you can understand that any form of entertainment is very welcome. It was with this in mind that we decided to try the entertainment approach to health education in the villages. At our first trial . . . a party from the hospital put on a programme of puppet show, small play, songs—in fact, a sort of mini-variety show—but all with a moral—predominantly a family planning one this time, but with other aspects of public health included. . . . There is no hall in the village, so it was performed in the open air, with this advantage—that all who wanted could see. In fact the whole village—men, women and children—to a total of over 1,200 people came and sat for nearly three hours—we commenced at 8.30 p.m.—and eagerly drank in all that was said and done. . . . This was but the beginning of a programme of regular per- formances, in the twelve villages we already visit weekly and spreading further afield. With such additions as film strips, movies, tape recordings and other publicity methods we will be able to educate many people to better health.

' Thank you very much, home league members. When you read of such medical advances in New Zealand as german measles vaccinations, think of your contribution to showing our village people how to prevent—by vaccination and clean living—such things as polio, tetanus, diphtheria, typhoid, T.B. and smallpox.'

Scholarships for medical and other training

A recent (1970) Salvation Army medical missionary newsletter issued from International Headquarters, mentioning the relatively few national Salvationist doctors (either officer or non-officer), intimates an important step being taken. 'We have recently informed each territory that suitable candidates will be granted scholarships for medical and other training. Such plans of progress cannot be expected to give quick results but we must be progressive and fulfil our determination to increase the number and quality of such trainees.

'Speaking in an historical sense, the third generation of missionaries is still essential, with an increasing number of national missionaries working side by side. We look forward (D.V.) to the fourth generation of *national* Salvation Army officer-doctors generally taking over charge in the present so-called developing countries and sharing fully our common task in all countries of preaching the gospel and healing the sick in Christ's name.'

Encouragement of interest in specific projects

There is an increasing sense of responsibility and concern in our day for the less fortunate, which shows itself in many ways. The current number of the Food & Agricultural Organization Review, *Ceres*, considers the problems of such help under the title, 'Aid or Co-operation'. No aid that does not result in active co-operation has long-term value, so a major emphasis in our planning now is the training of national staff, as already explained. In this programme we have received major help already from a number of joint church or other charitable organizations, e.g. Algemeen Diaconaal Bureau in Holland, which recently gave a grant for our new Training Centre for Handicapped Women in Aramboly connected with the Catherine Booth Hospital, Nagercoil, under the direction of Captain George Scott; and generous help for many other projects has been received from Oxfam, Simavi, Emmaus Suisse, Bread for the Brethren and others.

There is an important new development in Norway, Holland and Germany, by which the Government—in co-operation with a Joint Churches Committee—allocates funds for approved medical, educational and agricultural projects. So far, we have received generous help from the Norwegian Agency toward our Nurses' Training School in Nidubrolu and the extension of the T.B. work in Ahmednagar, and from the Dutch Agency for planned development of our work at Surabaja Hospital, Indonesia. We have further applications pending to the Dutch Agency, and others planned to the German Agency. Such grants, when approved, will provide seventy-five per cent of the cost of a modernization programme in relation especially to nurses' training schools in several hospitals.

The Joint Mission Hospital Equipment Board

This is a new and truly ecumenical venture to seek to provide *all* missionary and other charitable hospitals in the developing countries with good equipment at a tenth to a third of the normal cost.

Pioneering work in this field led to the formation, in 1965, of the Joint Mission Hospital Equipment Board, of which Sir John Richardson, Bart., M.V.O., M.D., F.R.C.P. is the Chairman, Dr. James Burton, the Medical Director, and Colonel Reginald Bovan, the Administrator, using a shed of The Salvation Army's Spa Road Centre, Bermondsey. The Board is now well established and meets the need for equipment not only of many mission hospitals, but also of the major charities in connection with emergency programmes. It is now being registered as a charity with excellent new premises in Sutton, Surrey.

Some Swedish medical missionary aid projects

Sweden is one of the territories of Salvation Army work which has long shown a lively and practical interest in missionary endeavours. Recent years have seen a number of projects among young people and others for aid to medical and other services overseas, particularly those involving Swedish officers.

In connection with the Fiftieth Anniversary of the Salvation Army Girl Guide Movement in Sweden, the Guides, wanting to mark the occasion with a special project, decided to raise funds to build an eye clinic at the Catherine Booth Hospital in Nagercoil, South India. Guides in Sweden sold over 200,000 ball-point pens in aid of the effort, giving a profit of around 100,000 Swedish kroner. It was thereafter possible for an up-to-date clinic to be dedicated in the presence of the Swedish Ambassador, Professor Gunnar Hecksher, and the Swedish Bishop, Gustaf Diehl.

When plans were being made for a bandsmen's congress in Linköping in May, 1970, it was proposed to make a special endeavour, apart from the purely musical aspect of the congress, and following inquiries put to Commissioner Jacobus Corputty, Territorial Commander for Indonesia, it was decided that the bandsmen would themselves undertake to raise 50,000 Swedish kroner toward the building of a hospital in Celebes (Sulawesi) where two Swedish Salvation Army officers, now promoted to Glory, Major Nanna Roslund and Major Hildur Palm, had given a lifetime of service. The hospital would not only perpetuate their memory, it was felt, but serve the needs of the local people in a practical way.

The project has involved not only personal giving, but the arranging of musical festivals and other special efforts in order to raise the necessary funds. Undoubtedly this is bringing a good deal of joy to the bandsmen themselves, and will prove a long term investment in the Kingdom of Heaven. It may well be that Salvationists of other countries will want to follow Sweden's example.

With the various encouragements in the fields of medical resources that the last ten years have brought, the essential need to maintain and develop Christian medical service is the commitment of men and women, from the so-called developed and from the developing countries, doctors, nurses, pharmacists, hospital secretaries, radiographers, physiotherapists, laboratory technicians and others, to take on the mantle of those who have been pioneers and of those who have followed on.

A recent arrival in India, a doctor who combines the outlook of a qualified surgeon with an absorbing interest in community health work, said: ' The future of the hospital work is really very exciting. When I tell you that in our district there are something like one and a quarter million people and only 350 hospital beds available for those number of people—and we have 110 in our hospital—that will give you some idea of the size of the task that we can set ourselves. When I further say that for this one and a quarter million people there are only two surgeons, of whom I am one, you will see that there is a great deal of work that can be done. . . .

' We have to take our services, and particularly our education, to the people where they are, and that means in their homes; we have to develop community health preventative medicine, rather than have an isolated hospital curative medicine service.'

Dr. Blenos Pedersen, graduate of the University of Toronto, who, in order to render service at Chikankata Hospital, Zambia, studied for the Academic Diploma (D.C.M.T.) at the London University School of Tropical Medicine and Hygiene, having previously practised in Canada for five years, has written: ' New Testament Christianity has a radical effect on one's life once it gets a hold on you. There is only one thing . . . to know the will of God and do it. . . . We cannot know the future will of God, even such things as the on and on growth of the Army or some particular work . . . but each man can *know* the will of God for today and be secure in the fact that all the tomorrows safely belong also to the will of God.'

I heard the voice of the Lord,
saying, Whom shall I send, and
who will go for us? Then said
I, Here am I; send me. (Isaiah 6: 8)

BIBLIOGRAPHY

1. BAIRD, Catherine, *Little Doctor, V.C.* (Salvationist Publishing & Supplies, Ltd., 1944).
2. *The Salvation Army Year Book,* 1966.
3. *The War Cry,* December 8, 1900.
4. *The Officer,* June 1918.
5. *All the World,* September 1917.
6. WILLIAMS, Harry, F.R.C.S., *The Shy Soldier,* unpublished MS.
7. GAUNTLETT, S. Carvosso, *He Gave Sight to Hundreds* (S.P. & S., 1948).
8. WILLE, Johannes, *Lys og Mørke* (Copenhagen, 1950).
9. UNSWORTH, Madge, *Great Was the Company.* (S.P. & S., 1963).
10. WIGGINS, Arch R., *The History of The Salvation Army, Vol. V* (Nelson, 1968).
11. *All the World,* August 1913.
12. AH KOW, Adelaide, *Mary Layton.* (S.P. & S., 1957).
13. HANSEN, Lillian, *The Double Yoke.* (The Citadel Press, New York, 1968).
14. WILLIAMS, Harry, F.R.C.S., *Miracle of Medicine Hill.* (S.P. & S., 1970).
15. WAITE, John, *The White Gujerati.* (*The War Cry,* London, September 17, 1966–February 27, 1967).
16. ATKINSON, John, *Dr. Beer Returns.* (S.P. & S.).
17. NEEVE, Ethel, *Nurse by Royal Command.* (S.P. & S., 1958).
18. TOUT, Kenneth, *Mary of Vendaland.* (S.P. & S., 1966).
19. *All the World,* January-March, 1971.
20. *The Officer,* October 1970.
21. *The Salvation Army Year Book,* 1969.
22. BRIDSON, Thomas, *Lightening the Lepers' Load.* (S.P. & S., 1946).
23. GAUNTLETT, Sidney, *Leprosy Control in the Southern Province of Zambia.* (*Lepr. Rev.* (1969) 40 pp., 223-232).
24. *All the World,* October-December, 1970.
25. *The Officer,* January-February, 1967.
26. *The Officer,* March-April, 1967.
27. *The Officer,* May-June, 1967.
28. *The Officer,* July-August, 1967.
29. *The Officer,* November-December, 1967.